BRITISH MINING No. 38

# A
# HISTORY OF THE MANOR
# AND
# LEAD MINES OF MARRICK,

This book is to be returned on or before
the last date stamped below.

**DED**

D1615712

LIBREX —

1

NORTHERN MINE RESEARCH SOCIETY

ISSN: 0308 2199
ISBN: 0 901450 35 9

Typeset in 10 on 11 point Bembo

Printed

by

RYTON TYPING SERVICE

29 Ryton Street, Worksop

Notts.

for the

publishers

**THE NORTHERN MINE RESEARCH SOCIETY
SHEFFIELD, ENGLAND.**

British Mining No. 38

# CONTENTS

© L. O. Tyson 1989.

Portal of Pryce Level with the mine office in the background. This was the site of the last attempt at underground working in this ancient mining field.

# ACKNOWLEDGEMENTS

I WOULD LIKE TO EXPRESS MY SINCERE THANKS TO Mr. C.D.W. Sheppard, Keeper of the Brotherton Collection at Leeds University for making available the Marrick Priory papers for study. These papers have revealed much new information on early mining at Marrick and also on the Cupuloe Smelt Mill which, up till now, has been something of an enigma to mining historians. Mr. Sheppard has made unstinting efforts to make these papers available for study, often outside his normal working hours and for all this kindness I shall always be in his debt; a rare man with a deep understanding of the problems faced by researchers.

A big thankyou to Mrs. Daphne Coates for allowing me to copy and quote from the Hurst Candle, Powder and Day Books which has allowed dates to be put to all the major development at Hurst from 1827 to 1850.

My thanks are also due to Mr. M. Y. Ashcroft, the County Archivist for North Yorkshire and those who have placed records in the Northallerton County Records Office for permission to study and use information gained from these records in the following Monograph. My thanks also to the good natured and friendly staff at Northallerton for all their kindness and assistance during my "holidays" spent with them.

Thanks are also due to Miss Hartley and Miss Ingleby for permission to quote from the Fawcett Account Book for 1663 and which is now deposited at the North Yorkshire County Records Office.

I gratefully acknowledge permission by R. J. Hanby Holmes and the Durham Records Office to quote from two leases in the Hanby Holmes M.S.S. Ref. No.s D/HH/6/4/100 and D/HH/6/4/121.

My very special thanks are given to Mike Gill for his valuable assistance in preparing the references and overseeing the Monograph prior to publication.

I am also grateful to the following people for information and encouragement, Dr. Arthur Raistrick, Mr. Howard Rule, Clarice Bray, Mr. A. E. Bray, O.B.E., Ian Spensley, Mrs. R. J. Freedman, Mr. Ralph Waggett, Lawrence Barker, Mr. N. Higson, University of Hull Archivist.

## INTRODUCTION

T HE MANOR OF MARRICK LIES AT THE MOUTH OF Swaledale in the old North Riding of Yorkshire. Situated on the north bank of the River Swale, the western boundary climbs up Reels Head to the distinct boundary wall which parallels Fremington Edge as far as Awkmay Cragg above Slei Gill, then bears east to St. Andrews Cross along Moresdale Ridge and down to Holgate Beck. Here, the boundary turns south to the hamlet of Helwith then across Skelton Moor to the Green Lane which it follows as far as Bradhow or Dales Beck below Cock How. This beck then forms the eastern boundary till it joins the Swale near Oxque, the river then forming the southern boundary.

Although Marrick village is the main settlement, it has remained throughout its history as a mainly agricultural centre, but owing to its proximity to the smelt mills, the smelters have tended to reside here. The 1871 census shows four smelters still living, two of whom, the Longstaffs, were both aged 60 which demonstrates that their's was not always a deadly trade.

The area where the present hamlet of Hurst and the Hurst Veins are situated was, from early times, known as Readhurst, while Shaw was an early vaccary of the Priory. These two hamlets, along with Washfold, were creations of the mining industry and grew in size as the mines expanded.

The population of Marrick manor slowly increased in size from 474 in 1801 to a peak of 415 just for the three hamlets of Hurst, Washfold and Shaw in 1841. This figure steadily declined to 152 in 1881 when whole families began to move away in search of work. The population in 1971 for the whole of Marrick was 86. The census also indicates that the miners were by 1871 trying to cushion themselves against this decline and many are shown as miner/farmers. Shaw and Washfold are now marked by heaps of rubble while the houses of Hurst have become the inevitable holiday home.

The Priory of Black Nuns, with its lands and mines, plays an important role in this history, mainly because of the complications which arose after its Dissolution in 1541 when the priory lands and those of the manor descended through different families.

The story is made even more intricate owing to the fact that Marrick was a strong Catholic area and the people adopted many devious methods in order to hide ownership and avoid fines or confiscation during the persecutions of the 17th century. Readers will have to approach this period with patience but the twists and turns of history will reveal a very strange story indeed for this apparently reserved manor.

There is now an air of quiet solitude lying over the upland reaches of Marrick which belies the fact that this is an area which has been governed by a thriving lead industry stretching back to the time of the first settlement in the Dales.

Opposite Hurst the two engine chimneys and the vast spoil heaps sweeping up to Fremington Edge stand as a mute reminder to man's effort in this upland fastness.

## CHAPTER 1

## GEOLOGY AND THE MINES

### *A brief description*

THE IMPORTANCE OF MARRICK LIES IN THE FACT THAT IT is in this area that the major veins which form the backbone of the North Swaledale mining field die out. The Wellington/Racca Vein, a continuation of the Friarfold/Great Blackside Veins, passes through the Fell End Mines above Slei Gill in Arkengarthdale, and, upon reaching the Hind Rake Vein turns south east and breaks up into a half mile wide belt of very rich veins and strings. These are mainly concentrated opposite the hamlet of Hurst but, upon reaching the strong cross fault known as Wallnook Vein near the Hurst/Marrick road, they are cut off with no veins appearing on the other side of this fault. It is this concentration of veins, plus the Copperthwaite Vein to the south, which forms the basis for this historical study of Marrick.

The strata at Hurst belongs to the standard Yoredale series and dips gently westwards from the high point of Fremington Edge. It is evident from the section of the mines that only the upper beds were fully worked, the 12 Fms or Main Lime and the Undersett Lime and Chert, which have proved so productive at Pryes and in other parts of the Swaledale field were never fully exploited. Therefore it is likely that there is a great deal of ore-bearing ground at Hurst still workable.

South east of the Wallnook Vein there are only two strong veins worked, Shaw and Pryes. Shaw Level, driven sometime before 1782[1] starts opposite the old hamlet of Shaw and tried the area towards Wallnook Vein. It was driven back from two shafts (see plan) which connected up with a drive in from the bank of Shaw Beck. Two sharp bends in the level indicate bad dialling. The level is driven in limestone for its full length and is now much reduced in size due to deads being stacked on the floor and against the walls.

Pryes Mine is the largest working to the south of Wallnook Vein. Deep whim shafts originally worked the Pryes North and Shaw Veins but problems with water caused a level to be started in 1859. This level lies at the lowest horizon on the field, but due to the strate being thrown down by Wallnook Vein, the Main Lime was not worked, (see section) but it is evident from the number of rises that the lower beds were extremely mineralised. The main workings were below the entrance adit to a depth of 45 Fms and were drained by a hydraulic engine. This raised the water to a drainage level, 6 fms below the adit, which ran off into a natural swallow in the broken ground on Shaw Vein and the draught created by the swallow played a major part in ventilating the mine.

South of Pryes, the ground was tried by several shafts and a short level below Greeenas Farm. North west of the Marrick Smelt Mills a short trial was made on the Musgrave Pasture Vein, but stopped soon after running into shale, there being no lead ore present only a strong calcite vein in the roof.

Short trial adits in Wild Sike on Smeltings Vein, and in Marrick Barf on the Marrick Great Vein are the most southerly trials, apart from one or two isolated

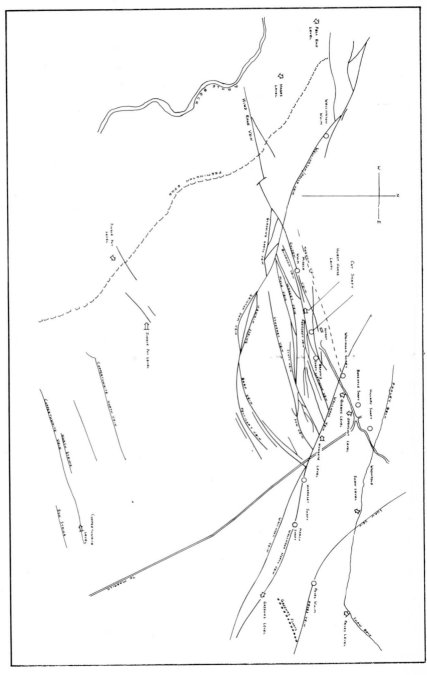

Fig. 1. Plan of veins at Hurst showing level mouths and main shafts. Not to scale.

shafts on Glittering Scar Vein south of the village of Marrick.

Returning north, up the western side of the manor, the Copperthwaite Vein was worked from both sides of the manorial boundary by deep shafts, opencasts and a hush at the eastern end of the vein. The density of these shafts testifies to the lengthy period of working and the richness of the vein, which was noted for its flatts which occurred near the boundary wall. The last attempt to exploit the vein was the driving of Copperthwaite Level in 1827. This was driven west from a point above the Hurst/Marrick road, and not as suggested by Dunham and Wilson who have misinterpreted the plan[2]. The size of the tips suggests that the old man had worked out the ground.

North of Copperthwaite, the Jingle Pot Vein was also worked on both sides of the boundary by several shafts and a short level driven westwards from near Owlands House.

We now return to the main Hurst complex where the ground was once again worked from a very early period by a great spread of shafts. As shown in a lease of 1718 (see text) several deep shafts were connected by crosscuts to a main drainage level referred to as the Water Level. This level was, by 1718, 500 Fms in length and must have been started at least 60 years previous to this date taking into account the distance driven[3]. It is possible that the miners encountered a cave system which drained into an underground swallow in the faulted ground near Washfold. Recognising the advantage they merely enlarged upon this feature and utilised it to their best advantage. There does not appear to be another explanation as to how they could have known of the existence of this swallow. Similar swallows were also used to drain the Golden Vein Rulleyway (see section) which also occurs in the Main Lime, and at Pryes.

The surface topography at Hurst, with its gently sloping hillside and no surface water to speak of, was ill suited for the kind of hushing used to advantage in other parts of Swaledale. The Sun Hushes near Nungate being the only examples of this method used on the main Hurst field. This topography also meant that any level driven would not gain any great depth and consequently were used for exploration and haulage purposes only. The main access was from deep surface shafts connected to the levels and from underground sumps and crosscuts.

The first adits driven at Hurst were the Nungate, prior to 1782, and Opencast. Hurst Horse Level, the highest level at Hurst was started by Josias Morley sometime after 1816 and was driven west towards Wellington Whim which was working the Wellington/Racca Vein near the boundary with Fell End and was eventually connected with the Fell End Mines.

Queens Level, started in 1836, was the last major development at Hurst being used once again as a haulage and exploratory level with a centralised dressing floors at its portal.

Moresdale Ridge is the northern boundary at Marrick and the ground was tried here by two levels. Porter Level, started in 1844, was driven south from the side of Moresdale Beck and the Moresdale Ridge Level, begun in 1836, was driven north from Skegdale. Both these levels encountered highly contorted ground and it is unlikely they produced much mineral.

## CHAPTER 2

## THE EARLY PERIOD AT MARRICK

RESEARCH BY DR. ARTHUR RAISTRICK IN THE 1930s AND more recent work by Laurie and Fleming has shown that first settlement of the upland areas around Marrick began during the Second Millenium B.C.[4] Evidence for this consists of concentrations of parallel reave systems and house foundations on Copperthwaite Allotments, Fremington Haggs and Cock How. There are barrows and cup and ring stones further north on Holgate Moor and How Tallon.

A tradition has grown that Hurst was used as a Roman Penal Colony, using slave labour to work for lead. The basis for this speculation, first reported by H. Speight in his book *Romantic Richmondshire* printed in 1897, is the reputed finding of a pig of lead stamped with the name of the Roman Emperor Adrian[5]. This pig, supposed to be in the British Museum, cannot now be located despite efforts to trace it by Miss Hartley and Miss Pontefract in the late 1940s. There is no archaeological evidence at present to show that the Romans made any attempt to occupy the area between their fort at Bainbridge in Wensleydale and the fort at Bowes, although it is likely they had a road connecting these two forts. If this pig of lead ever did exist it could, like the hoard of Roman Horse equipment found hidden on Fremington Edge, have been left by Brigantian raiders based at Maiden Castle on Harkerside. Until more definate archaeological work proves a Roman presence in the Swaledale area it is perhaps better that this tradition be laid to rest.

The major settlement came during the Anglo Saxon period when the proximity of the village to the massive Brigantian Dyke, which crosses the mouth of Swaledale, could have given rise to the name of the village which in Anglo Saxon means boundary village, "Maer" "Wicka"[6]. Given the expertise in metal working of these peoples it is highly likely that they found surface deposits of galena and exploited them.

At the time of Domesday, Marrick or Mange as it was recorded, contained 5 carrucates for geld, had two ploughs and was worth 5s although it was described as waste, as were most of the villages in the area. Previous to the Conquest the manor was held by Archil under Earl Edwin as part of the kingdom of Mercia. When Duke William found himself unable to govern the Dales in the period following the Harrying of the North he leased the manor to Gospatric, one of the few surviving English Earls who were tolerated by the Normans.

Soon after 1100 the Normans began to attempt an effective government of the Dales and the Manor of Marrick was granted to Roger Aske in return for Knight Service to Earl Conan at his castle in Richmond, and it was to remain in the hands of this family for the next 400 years.

Roger Aske, grandson of the above Roger, founded a priory for Benedictine Nuns about 1165 on a shoulder of land above the River Swale formed by an old river terrace and gave them a third of the vill of Marrick for the upkeep of

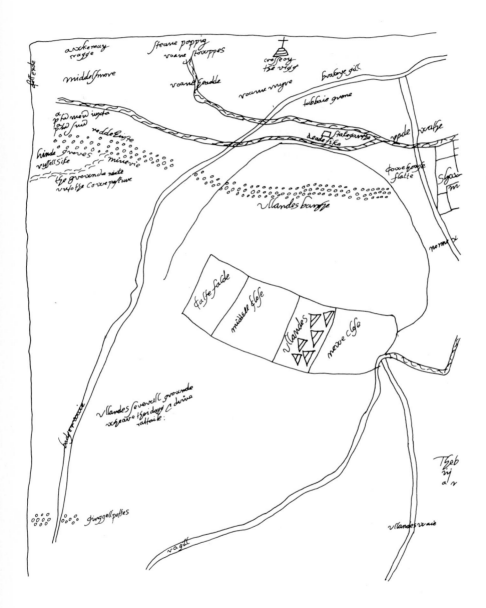

*Fig. 2. Map of the Hurst area circa 1592 which shows the spread of shafts on Hindrake, Redhurst and Owlands Barf.*
*(Brotherton Collection).*

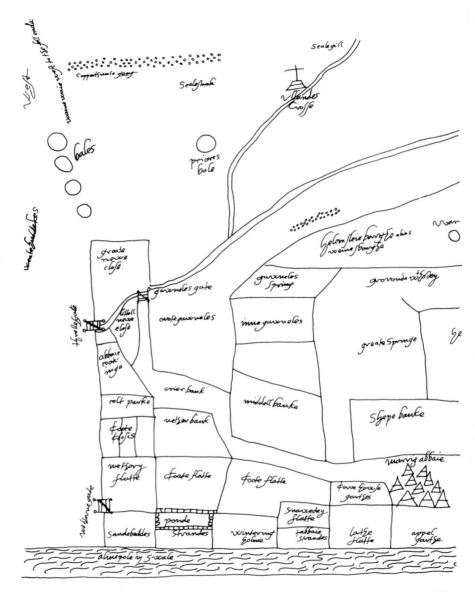

*Fig. 3. Map of the Copperthwaite area circa 1592 which clearly shows bale hills including that used for smelting the Priory ore. This bale can still be located but slags from the other bales were taken away to be smelted at Marrick Mill in the 1660s. This is the only known map showing bale hills in the Swaledale area and is therefore unique. (Brotherton Collection).*

the Priory. Through the years the Nuns received further bequests of land and tithes both in Marrick and other parts of Yorkshire, including the keeping of the Hospital on Stainmore. They also looked after the corn mill on the river for the Aske's and shared in the lead mines by receiving a tithe of lead ore due to the Rectory of the church of St. Andrew which had been part of the original grant, an earlier chapel being incorporated into the Priory.

The building of the Priory gives us the first documented evidence of lead mining at Marrick[7]. Stone for the buildings was obtained from quarries at Awkmay Craggs, Roanmire, and Skegdale. Lead for roofing was got from mines established "from time out of minde" at Copperthwaite, Blakey How, Redd Hurst, Grenehowse and Ullandes Barf. Even at this early date the mines were so well established that they could provide and smelt sufficient lead to cover the church, frater, dorter, cloister, closset and other smaller buildings.

In 1512, William the last male Aske died leaving his two daughters as co-heirs. Elizabeth, wife of Richard Bowes received one third of the manor plus other lands, and Anne, wife of Sir Ralph Bulmer of Wilton, held the other two thirds as her portion. On the death of Elizabeth in 1535 her one third share passed to Anne uniting Marrick in the hands of the Bulmer family.[8].

## The Bulmer Family

Sir Ralph Bulmer was the second son of Sir William Bulmer of Wilton. His elder brother Sir John was hanged at Tyburn in 1537 for his part in the Pilgrimage of Grace and his wife was Margaret burnt at the stake.

Sir Ralph held the majority of the mines which were at Copperthwaite, Red Hurst, Grenehowse, Seal Gill, Bleakey How and Owlands Barf. The nuns had their own shafts on the above veins raising an average of 8 or 9 fothers of lead annually.

The mines were not worked directly by Sir Ralph but leased out to small partnerships. Richard Bowes had a meer of ground at Red Hurst, Christopher Conyers, lord of the neighbouring manor of Marske, had another meer of ground at Red Hurst and in his will made in 1504 left to "William my son a more mere at Coupperthwaite, which I bought of Thomas Metcalfe"[9]. Ralph Gower of Richmond had meers at Red Hurst and Grenehowse. Richard Hutchinson of Skelton and several other partnerships of men from Marske, Skelton, Arkengarthdale and New Forest were also working various shafts. The usual royalty paid to the Bulmers was either one third or one fourth but they also received the ninth load which was known as "lott lode".

Most of the smelting was carried out at the bales situated to the south of Copperthwaite (see map). The nuns had their own bale, the prioress's bale, and this can still be located east of the O.S. Trig Point.

Here again, Sir Ralph leased out the rights to grave turves, pull ling and gather wood at Dead Syke, Hazelhowe and Hawthornes. The fuel for the bales was mentioned in a boundary dispute of 1502 between Roger Aske and Christopher Conyers when Adam Spensley of Owlands gave evidence that "he hathe seen the Askes and Bulmers, owners of the manors of marrigge, cut downe, carrye away, and burne at theire lead bales such wodde as grewe apon Hazelhowe and Hawthornes"[10].

The only known record of early mining law in Swaledale, the laws and customs by which mining at Marrick was governed, was quoted in a dispute of 1574. Customary Mining law is generally thought to have originated in the Anglo-Saxon period but the earliest written example, from Derbyshire, dates from 1288. In Yorkshire, the oldest set of laws were those recorded at Grassington in 1642 and it was once thought that the Wharfedale liberties, especially those of Grassington and Buckden with Starbotton, were the only ones in the county where such laws applied. A recent paper, however, proposed that "Until the early seventeenth century, when it was discontinued, a form of Customary Law, with its associated privileges, extended throughout much of the Dales."[11] The importance of this document is, therefore, sufficient to justify its full transcription:-

first when the mine is fownde of newe in the moores, the marchantes and miners shall chose theime a barghe master otherwise callide a moore master for to deliver to the finders of the mine ij meares under a stake, and oone meare to the lorde nexte unto the same finders/

and afterwarde the moore master shall deliver the saide felde to the miners bi certaine meares to theime that will worke theime after the lawe of mine/

and after that the lorde of the fielde and the miners shall ordeine a coverable dishe bi the which the lordde shall receave his lotte and the miners there right of the mine/

that is the miners eight dishes and the lorde the ninthe, and the chirche the tenth/

and the miners abiding and conversante apon the mine shall have sufficient howsebote and hedgebote and all maner of timber for theire groves, bi the deliverie of the lorde or his forrester, if he have sufficient within the lorde shippe/

and if none maie be fownde within the lorde shippe, and thei be providid for timber at theire costes in other plasis out of the lorde shippe then the lorde shall nothing take for his lotte/

hearre note that the lotte ure is given for timber wodde to be hadde to the groves / and not for anie titell or right that the lorde hathe in the mine, more than a nother miner/

which being plaine then the finders, and other that will worke be as free to have a meare of grownde as the lorde, if the moore master will so deliver it/

and in this sortte the priores of marrigge, hadde all waies her meares of grownde deliverede to her in divers plasis apon the more of marrigge bi the more masters from time to time, as often as anie newe mine or fielde was fownde/

and the saide meares of grownde be yet knowen to this daie apon the moore of marrigge/

as at coppthwate redde hirste ullandes barghe sele gill blokey howes and grenenose/

and all thiese meares of grownde thei ever hadde severallie to theire owne usis/

besides the tythe of everie meare of grownde that was wrought apon the moore/

## The Dissolution of The Priory and The Uvedale Family

In 1536 Henry VIII began the suppression of the monasteries and Marrick was one of the houses valued at less then £200. The events of the Pilgrimage of Grace delayed the surrender for some time and the nuns managed to hold out till 1540 when the prioress Christabell Cowper surrendered the house on the 17th November 1540. She and the sixteen nuns were granted pensions and thrown out to fend for themselves as best they could.

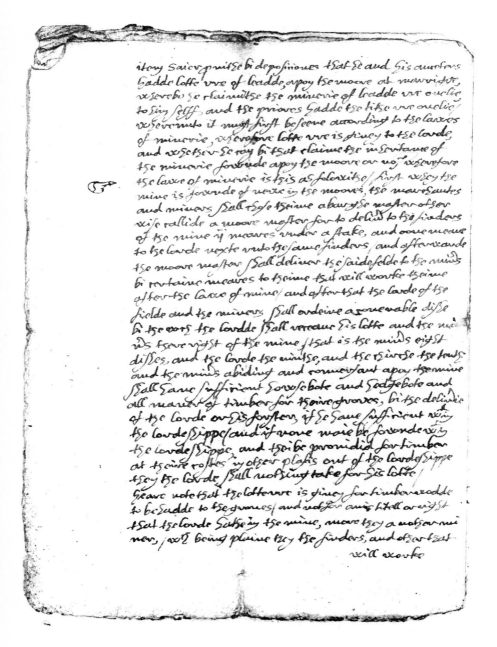

*Fig. 4. Mining laws of 1574/5.*

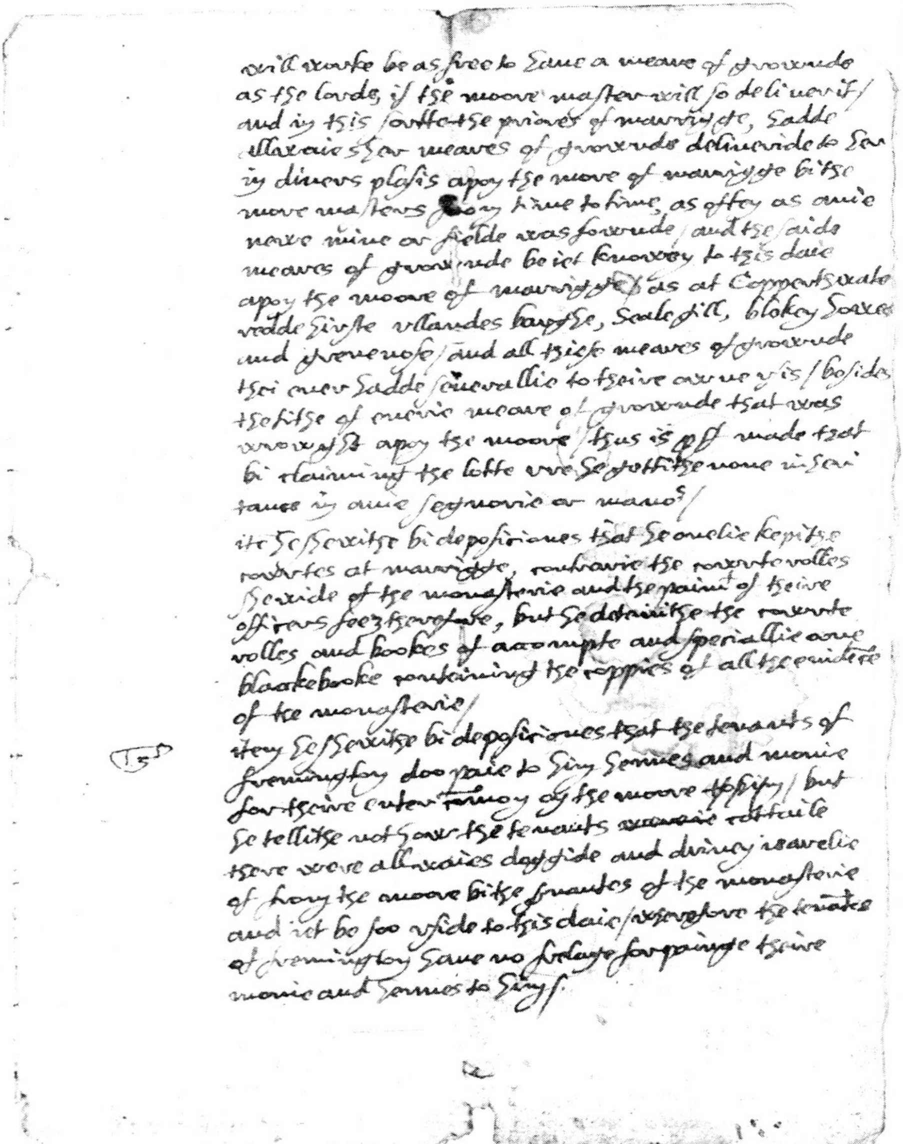

Fig. 4a. Mining laws 1574/5.

The two commissioners who received the surrender were Leonard Beckwith and John Uvedale. Both these men were opportunists and not averse to gaining from their situation. Beckwith ended up owning the lands of Handale Abbey in Cleveland, was knighted in 1544 and married Theophania, daughter of Sir Marmaduke Grimston of Kildwick, Co. York.

John Uvedale was also a perfect example of a man of his times and as he was to play an important role in the affairs of Marrick it may be of interest to detail his rise to power.

His career began in 1488 when he was commissioned to provide horses and carts for the transport of the Royal household and in 1513 was entrusted with the Commissariat at Flodden. This brought him to the attention of Henry VIII who raised him to the rank of Esquire and in 1516 he became Clerk of the Pells in the Exchequor. This post gave him an insight into the profits to be gained from mining and in 1529 he obtained a lease of all the coal and iron mines in the Forest of Teesdale at 1/20th, and in 1533, along with his good friend the all powerfull Thomas Cromwell, took a fifty year lease of all the mines on Dartmoor. In 1537 he obtained a lease of the lead mines of Nidderdale from the soon-to-be-dissolved Byland Abbey[12]. He then sublet the mines to the Earl of Cumberland and James Fromount.

When John Uvedale came to view Marrick he must have found it difficult to contain himself for here was a house with tithes of lead due to the rectory worth £30 p.a. and their own lead mines. Unfortunately Cromwell's star began to wane in 1540 so without his powerful patron Uvedale had to wait till 1543 for a 21 year lease of the priory and its lands. As he was very prominent in the prosecution of those involved in the Pilgrimage of Grace, Sir Ralph Bulmer's brother being executed, visits to Marrick cannot have been pleasant for him.

In the meantime Sir Ralph Bulmer had not been idle, obtaining, from the Prioress, leases of Owlands and other lands in Marrick vill[13]. The Prioress had also granted leases of the Spittall on Stainmore and corn tithes due from the villages of Downholme, Carkin and Aiskew.

Immediately upon obtaining his lease of the priory Uvedale, who was now Secretary to the Council of the North, laid a complaint about these leases before the Council and it is hardly suprising that they were soon declared void due to a clause in the Act of Dissolution which rendered any lease made since 1536 illegal.

Uvedale, in 1545, replaced Sir Ralph Salder as treasurer for the garrisons in the north and became known locally as the richest man in Swaledale. He purchased outright from the Crown the site and demesne of Marrick Priory in 1545 for £364-6d.

John Uvedale died in December 1549 and was succeeded by his son Avery who was married to Ann Babyngton, daughter of the Warden of the Fleet and was also prominent in public life. He was styled as "serjeant at law and one of the gentlemen ushers of our chambers" in Letters Patent which granted him in 1551 the office of Bow Bearer for the New Forest and Arkengarthdale, although he derived little profit from this office. He also obtained the rectory of East Grinton on the opposite bank of the Swale and was a Justice of the Peace.

Sir Ralph Bulmer died in 1554 and his daughter carried their holdings in Marrick to her husband John Sayer of Worsall near Yarm in which family it was to remain for two generations.

Avery Uvedale brought an action against Sir John Yorke in 1554 alleging that Yorke had stolen from his mines in Nidderdale 36 loads of lead ore weighing 675 cwts[14]. Quoted in this case are some unusual weights for lead, "A lode of leade dothe consist of 30 Formells, a Formell being six stone except 2 powndes and every stone doth consist of 12 powndes by which the sume in the Formell is 70 powndes". Avery reckoned that the 36 loads would have given him "7 fowthers of lead Ewre which is nowe worthe to be soulde for viij^Li everye fowther".

History, however, played the trump card for Avery lost his case plus the lease of the mines because of the clause in the Act of Dissolution which cancelled all leases made by dissolved houses; the very act which his father John had used to obtain the lands at Owlands etc. leased to Sir Ralph Bulmer.

This was only the beginning of litigation in which Avery was to become involved. Several boundary disputes brought by him against the Sayers and the Phillips family who held Marske at this time. These disagreements were further fuelled by religious differences, for the Uvedale's were Protestants and Marrick, under the Bulmers and Sayers, was a staunch catholic stronghold.

The mines attached to Owlands were managed for Avery in 1561 by his agent Henry Boardman who let bargains and also purchased ore for smelting from various miners including Geofrey Willow and Leonard Close of Blades and Adam Spensley of Marrick, whose father William had been shepherd at Owlands for the nuns since Flodden. The bargains made with the miners contained a curious penalty clause, for on failure to deliver ore they had to pay a sum of money or cattle to Avery's wife.

The effects of the last great rising of the north in 1569/70 were felt at Marrick when several rebels, including Bryan Carter and William Allanson of Arkengarthdale and William Arundell of Healaugh, attacked Avery's house at Owlands and in November broke the communion plate in Marrick church and assaulted and robbed the curate William Pratt.

Sometime in 1574/5, John Sayer built the first smelt mill at Marrick by the side of Dales Beck[15]. This is confirmed by evidence given in several boundary disputes. William Hawkyn of Healaugh aged 72, deposed that "indede the said defendant (John Sayer) hath taken away one of the said springes (from Stelling Dub) and turnide the same to dryve a mill". Another witness stated that Sayer had enclosed the land "for buildinge of a mill there". In another case "the pl^ts have caused a water mylne a kylne and a dwelling howse to be buylded upon the said more". Although this evidence does not describe the mill as a smelt mill there are a number of factors that indicate it must have been for this purpose. There were no crops grown nearby to justify building a corn mill here but the proximity to the mines, access to the Richmond road for transport and the only available source of a large and regular water supply to turn the wheel for the bellows.

Trouble for Avery erupted again in 1580 when he wrote a letter of complaint to the Queen in which he alleged that John Sayer had incited a mob of 20 local man on the 20th of November "with great force and avries and in riotose manner and strong hand, with staves, daggers, iren pykes and pyccals and other defensible weapons, have entride in to a certain hill or barghe callide ullandis hill". There the mob dug several shafts and trenches, spoiling the pasture and took away lead ore to the value of £20. The Queen's council replied by ordering the local justices at Richmond to bind Sayer and the others on bonds of money to appear before the court at York. Poor Avery urged that the case be dealt with quickly "bicawse they be a multitude and may doe me bodilye hurtte"[18].

Avery Uvedale died on the 21st June 1583 leaving two sons, John and Thomas and a daughter Elizabeth. His widow Anne was left £100, John got the Marrick Estate and Thomas the lands in Carkyn, Aiskew and Downeholme. Five years later, John and Thomas sold Marrick to Richard Brakenbury of Sellaby, co. Durham for 200 marks. Brakenbury also held the site of Ellerton Priory on the other side of the Swale.

Richard Brakenbury sold the site of the priory and its lands on March 7th 1592 to Sir Timothy Hutton of Bishop Auckland, son of Mathew Hutton Archbishop of York, whose mother Elizabeth was a god-daughter of Queen Elizabeth.

## Marrick During The Civil War

A new family, the Blackburne's, come into the story in 1596 when Sir Timothy Hutton leased the Priory estates to Robert Blackburne, upholsterer of London for 21 years at an annual rental of £149-13-4d. Like their predecessors, the Uvedale's they too were destined to be unlucky in their holding of these lands; indeed the nuns seem to have put a curse on anyone who held the site of the priory. Mathew Hutton, Sir Timothy's father purchased the neighbouring manor of Marske in 1600 for £3,000 and in 1601 this passed to Sir Timothy.

The rest of Marrick continued to be held by the Sayer's until 1618 when a marriage contract was drawn up between Sir Bertram Bulmer of Thurdale, co. Durham and John Sayer of Worsall. This agreed that upon the marriage of William Bulmer, son of Sir Bertram and Dorothy, and the daughter and co-heir of John's brother George Sayer, then the manor would be settled on them along with the manor of Silkworth, co. Durham. Sir Bertram Bulmer was the son of Sir Ralph Bulmer's brother Sir William and so once again the manor passed back into the hands of the Bulmer family.

Sir Timothy Hutton died in 1629 and was succeeded by his son Mathew. Owing to heavy encumbrances on the estate, combined with his poor handling of money, Mathew was forced by debt to sell the Priory estate to the Blackburne family in 1630 for £3,800.

Along with the Priory estate, Robert Blackburne had the tithes of lead ore due to the rectory of St. Andrew Grinton. In 1631, as soon as he obtained full possession of the estate, he brought an action in the court at York alleging that William Bulmer, his father Sir Bertram and John Sayer had, from October 1630 to August 1631, occupied ground at Red Hurst and got 200 bings of ore for which they had paid no tithes. This was an attempt to legally enforce payment of the tithes but he seems to have met with little success for in 1634, on the 13th March, he conveyed the tithes to William Bulmer for £750. The tithes in 1535 were valued at 24/- but by 1625 the rent and tithes of the Priory were worth £250 yearly to Sir Timothy Hutton[17].

The effects of the two major conflicts of the 17th century, catholic persecution and the Civil War, began to be felt at Marrick. The Bulmers and Sayers were very strong catholics and as such were subjected to the various fines levied on known recussants, and as early as 1632, William Bulmer compounded as a recussant.

The system of fines and compounding led to many complicated manoeuvres to keep hold of their land by many of the North Riding gentry. To avoid losing Marrick, William Bulmer granted a 21 year lease of the lead mines in 1635 and part of the manor at 12d yearly rental to Sir Thomas Tempest of Stella, co. Durham, a relative by marriage, and Sir William Lambton, in return for clearing a debt of £4,938 which he had accrued due to the many fines made on him. In 1641 the tithes of lead were sold to George Scott.

The mines' lease descended to Lady Troth Tempest and when the Bulmers estate at Marrick was sequestered in 1654, she was forced to appeal to the Committee for Sequestrations to have the mines, and her part of the estate, discharged.

*Plate I. Fryers head, Winterburn near Skipton. Home of John Blackburne.*

The township of Marrick was assessed in 1646 for taxes and Christopher Copperthwaite, a major in the Militia, decided that for every 40s charged on the township the mines should pay 16s "as long as the said Lead Mynes shall continue good and workable". This order was ignored and in 1648 the inhabitants of Marrick complained to the Committee for the Militia that the township was worth only £500 yearly but the mines whose profits belonged partly to the township were not being paid by Lady Tempest who was receiving £1,000 annual profit for herself.

After the appeal by the people of Marrick in 1648 the Committee for Militia sent in agents to ensure that Lady Tempest payed the monies due from her mines. She in turn complained to the Committee for Compounding in 1650 that these agents were interfering with the running of the mines and preventing her agents from working them efficiently. The Committee replied by offering her two thirds of the mines and lands at £1,000 annually but she declined. The case dragged on till 1654 when her lease expired.

Meanwhile, the Bulmers were forced by mounting debts to transfer, in 1648, the Silkworth estate and the residue of the Marrick holdings, including the mines' lease to Thomas Swinburne of Barmeton, Co. Durham. He was a relative by marriage to the Bulmer and Tempest families.

In 1654, William Bulmer set about regaining that part of the Marrick estate not held by Thomas Swinburne. Acting through two lawyers, Gilbert Crouch and John Rushworth, an appeal was laid before the Surveyors for the Commonwealth and the lands were granted to Crouch and Rushworth who then transferred them to the Bulmers. These two lawyers made a rich living acting as professional nominees for Royalist and Recussant gentry to enable sequestered land to be returned back to the owners at a nominal rent.

Thomas Swinburne refused to honour the condition in the 1648 agreement that William Bulmer be allowed to repurchase at a future date his Marrick holdings, and so became the major landholder at Marrick. He also now owned the mines and the lead ore tithes which he had purchased from George Scott in 1652.

The Blackburne family down at Marrick Priory seem to have avoided the troubles of these turbulent years and came through unscathed.

## CHAPTER 3

## THE MARRICK MINES AND SMELT MILLS. 1660 to 1663.

IT IS EXTREMELY FORTUNATE THAT AN ACCOUNT/DAY book has survived for the period November 1660 to June 1663 which allows us to gain a great deal of information on this early period.[18]

The mines and the bulk of the Marrick estate were owned by Thomas Swinburne and managed for him by his agent John Fawcett, who was paid £51 : 13s : 4d annually with a Mr. Myles as his assistant. There were 23 miners employed at shafts on Red Hurst and Copperthwaite, many of whom were forebears of families that were still working in the mines 200 years later : Hillary, Waggett, Haykin, Hall, Elliott and March.

The mines were worked by shafts and sinking was paid for at daytale rates between 3 : 6d to 4s : 6d per fathom. Crosscuts were driven from the shafts at an average payment of 2s per fathom. For "beating" a shaft or level, which probably refers to dressing the rough sides and making them safe from loose stone, a rate of 18d per fathom was paid. Candles were sold to the miners at 6½d per pound, and "three bords for casting water of when they work in the groves" cost two shillings.

The accounts give a rare reference to the use of fire setting for breaking ground : "for carrying 3 quarts of coles to hurst to firewith in the levill at 4s per quarter = 12s". This firesetting was probably being used in the driving of the Water Level, which must have been started around this time.

Unfortunately no reference is made to the method of raising ore from the shafts but "Harden" at 10d per yard was used for making chopsacks, ore pokes and water bags for "drawing water with in the groves".

Miners were paid 17/- to 18/- per bing of ore and they did their own dressing. Rinyell March had the highest payment for the amount of ore raised, receiving £60-2-9d for 70 bings from November 1660 to April 1661, and £66-6s for 77 bings from Nov 1661 to Nov 1662.

As with other mines, vast amounts of timber were required and frequent payments were paid to the miners for drawing out timber from old or abandoned workings. Wood was also purchased from surrounding landowners, Tristan Elliott being paid to travel round viewing prospective timber purchases. Stoprice was paid for by the horse load and chopwood for smelting cost an average of 5d per sack.

Both the High and Low Mills were working between 1660-63 and power for the bellows came from waterwheels. Several payments were made for repairs about the mills; "Thomas Hudson for mending yᶜ hye mill bellows and for mending yᶜ kilnhole doors", "Thos Hudson for sawing thornwood for tridles and tapps", "Thos Hudson for mending low mill bellowes, for mending the chimney and for putting in triddles and tapps", "pᵈ for dressing the goat betwixt the hye mill & low mill and yᶜ low mill goat", "pᵈ for 3 quarts of oyl for lickering the bellows at 15d pe quart", "Thos Hudson, his son, for mending the kilhole walls, for lyeing in 7 new Kilbauks".

The roof of the High Mill was damaged by high winds in 1661 and 150 slates costing 10/- were purchased from Leonard Addison's quarry above Healaugh. These cost 8d per horse load at 15 slates per horse and this occasion was used to make other repairs to the mills. The High Mill chimney was pointed using a bushel of hair in the lime and pointing the walls took 8 quarts of lime at 18d per quart. The Low mill had a new sumpter put in and the floor and hearth were repaired. Most of the joinery and building work was undertaken by Thomas Hudson of Fremington and his son Thomas. John Terry, one of the Jaggers, took care of any smith work at the mills.

Smelting was fairly well organised with an ore-hearth at the High Mill costing 7/- per fother for smelting and a slag hearth at the Low Mill costing 22/- per fother for smelting. For serving the High Mill with fuel etc it cost 22d per fother but the Low Mill was 8/- per fother.

Dressing the High Mill ashes cost 5d per piece and slags from the High Mill cost 20d per piece whereas "Blackworke" from the slag hearth cost 2/4d per piece. Also during this period, a great amount of slag was brought from the old bale hill sites on Fremington Edge for re-smelting in the slag hearth, a total of 925 horse loads at 3d per load. Loads were also brought from sites on Skelton Moor, a total of 158 horse loads at 3½d per load. Iron riddles costing 8d each were purchased for dressing the slags on the moors.

Coal, cinders and chopwood were the main fuels used at the mills as there are no entries for peat at this time. Cinders were brought to Cole Pit Moor above Hurst for burning at 2/6d per quarter by Ralph and William Maynard and coal for the High Mill cost 20d per quarter[19]. No indication is given as to the location of where the coal was purchased from but it was most probably from Tan Hill area. Chopwood for the mills was made from tree branches at the Kilnhold near the mills.

Life at the mines and mills was subject to interruption as can be seen from the following payments:- "Pd by Mr Myles at severall times to the smelters in drinks to in courridge them when Mr Hutton came and distrained the lead and threating them for working for Mr Swinburne", also Pd by Mr Miles at severall times amongst the workmen in drinks to incourridge them when Mr Hutton came and distrained there ore and grove ropes".

During this period, a total of 185 fothers of Swinburne's ore and 53 fothers and 4 pieces of ore for other mines were smelted at the mills. This ore was carried first to the mills near Hartforth near Gilling ready for carrying to Stockton. There were eight jaggers employed who were paid 6/8d per fother for carriage to Hartforth and 20d per piece when two fothers were sent to the Bishop of Durham at Auckland. The jaggers also carried slags to the mills from the bale hill sites and timber and wood for the mines and mills.

At Stockton, the agent was Mr. Pierce and prices per fother ranged from £10, £10-7-6d, £10-15s and £11.

Unfortunately, Thomas Swinburne does not appear to have made a great profit during this time, a total of £2678-10-1½d were the working costs and £2559-9-7½d were monies received for ore sold and the Marrick rents which left a profit of £119-6d from the mines.

## A New Owner

The business affairs of Thomas Swinburne were not very successful and by 1668 he was so far in debt that he was forced to sell the estate and mines at Marrick. The purchaser was Charles Powlett, Lord St. John of Basing, the son of the Marquis of Winchester. An agreement was signed on the 6th of March and from this it is possible to see the extent of the effort made by Swinburne to extricate himself from debt and which John the son of Thomas Swinburne, now living at Grays Inn, Middlesex was trying to sort out[20].

The Swinburnes were to get £5,000 but little of this was left after clearing various debts; £700 went to Walter Rea for a mortgage of £1,000 taken out in 1663, £575 to Dame Margaret Lee, £500 to Richard Piers, Swinburne's lead agent, and £725 in other debts, all of which Lord St. John had to pay himself and deduct from the purchase price. The mines had been leased in two parts, one half on the 29th May 1665/6 for 11 years at a payment of £220, plus an annual rental of £40, to Benjamin Purchas of Clints and Robert Jackson; the rest to Francis Chaplin, merchant tailor of London, on the 11th December 1666/7 for 12 years at 12d per annum for the first 7 years and £20 p.a. for the residue of the lease. The low first payment suggests that Swinburne had received a cash payment for the first 7 years. He had also granted several 1,000 year farm leases which greatly reduced the improved yearly rental on entry by the new landlord. This left John Swinburne - Thomas must have died during this time - and his wife Mary with £2,450.

William Bulmer died in 1668 and was succeeded by his son Anthony and a year later in 1669 Gyles Blackburne died leaving the Marrick Priory lands to his son John. Charles Powlett, the eldest son and heir apparent to John, Marquis of Winchester, acting through his trustees Mitford and Cratford, purchased the holding in Marrick of Anthony Bulmer for £2,500 on October 23rd 1671, thus giving him control of two thirds of Marrick plus the mines and bringing to an end the connection of the Bulmer family with Marrick.

In 1676, an agreement was drawn up between Charles Powlett, who had succeeded to the titles of Marquis of Winchester and Earl of Wiltshire in 1674, and Humphrey Wharton of Gilling Wood, who was lessee of the Manor of Fremington, regarding the lead veins which cross from Fremington into Marrick[21]

The Wayne Way, an ancient trackway which parallels Fremington Edge, was used as the boundary in this agreement. The first clause concerned the Jingle Pot Vein and 150 yards was to be measured east from the Wayne Way on this vein and the half nearest Marrick to belong to that manor and the half nearest Fremington to belong to that manor.

The next vein north along the Edge is Hindrake Vein and this also had 118 yards measured east from the Wayne Way and divided out in a like manner, with the proviso that all the ore raised by Humphrey Wharton's men be delivered dressed and ready for smelting to the Marrick Mills, and Powlett would pay 30/- per bing, the ore being measured using the standard measure which was in use at Copperthwaite.

These grants on the Marrick side of the Wayne Way were compensated for by a grant on the Fremington side of a 25 yard square meer on the very rich Copperthwaite Vein. This is the second documented reference to a meer and it was set out thus:-

"On the west side of that shaft on Copperthwaite Rake or Vayne called or known by the name of Bounder Shaft in and upon all such floats flatts or pipe workes as are already discovered, and all vaynes flats or pipes under them to a certayne shaft on the said Copthwate Rake towards Fremington, formerly wrought by John Simpson and Chris Hall / from a line to be drawn from the sayd Bounder Shaft in a direct lyne south or forward of 25 yards length and a like direct lyne drawne forth or forthward from the sayd shaft formerly wrought by John Simpson and Chr. Hall the length of 25 yards / And also that a direct lyne be drawne from the four end of the one 25 yard lyne to the four end of the other 25 yards lyne / And that the sayd Lord Marques shall have and enjoy to him, his heirs and ass[ns] for ever all the veins, pipes and floates of lead & lead oare within or under the compass of the layde lynes but noe other now further on the south or southwards thereof".

The nature of the Copperthwaite Vein, with its many rich flats, is illustrated in the lease. It was further agreed that a proper boundary be marked out with meer stones by Philip Swale, agent for Wharton, and William Orton the steward for Powlett "at equal charge" between the two manors.

On the 12th of February 1683 John Blackburne, who had inherited the Marrick Priory lands from his father Gyles in 1669, was compelled by debts and various mortgages taken out by his father and mismanagement by his trustees, his uncles Tymothy and Francis Blackburne of Grinton, to sell most of his lands to Charles Powlett for £1,778.

As with his purchase of lands from Swinburne, Charles Powlett had to first clear the mortgages of Gyles Blackburne taken out with the Metcalfe's of Fossdale and High Hall in Dent, and John and Leonard Smelt of Feetham, a total of £1,500 plus £45 interest, before the sale could go through, which left John Blackburne with only £184-16-9d.

Powlett also purchased all the woods and trees in Marrick which belonged as part of the Priory holdings from John Blackburne for £260, all the tithes due to the rectory for £236-8s and the lands of Leonard Spensley for £850. This left Powlett owning the whole of Marrick apart from the site of the Priory which John Blackburne held onto and Robert Bucktons land at Oxque and Reels Head.

Charles Powlet also took out leases on various veins on Grassington Moor at this time. He also appears to have been in a delicate position with the King, for in a letter written by Sir John Reresby on July 16th 1683, a mention is made that the Marquis used to hunt by torchlight among the cliffs and woods near Marske and feigned insanity for political reasons "in these ticklish times" and thereby preserve his estates.

He must have done well, however, "in these ticklish times" for in 1689 he was created Duke of Bolton and began building Bolton Hall in Wensleydale. A settlement made prior to the marriage of his second son William to Lady Lovese Armilius, the daughter of the Marquise de Mumpillian in Holland, the estates, with a reservation of the mines, were put in the hands of trustees and on the death of Charles in 1699, the mines, woods, plus lands in Marrick and Fremington passed to Lord William Powlett.

## The Affair of the Cupuloe Smelt Mill

John Blackburne had retained the site of the priory but was living in 1700 at Fryerhead near Gargrave, which he had inherited through his wife Francis, the daughter of Colonel Francis Malham.

With John Blackburne begins a very interesting period in the history of lead mining in the Dales that reveals a greater interaction between the various mining fields than previously realised.

Reuben Orton was Blackburne's agent at Marrick and was involved with Blackburne in trying to get partners to finance and build a new smelt mill at Marrick which they referred to as the Cupuloe[22]. In a letter to Blackburne dated 27th February 1700, Orton wrote that Theodore Bathurst of Arkengarthdale whose "mines will be very shortly in his and his partners hands, if soe he may prove a good partner to us, but in all this time I have but got fifteen pounds of Mr. Bathurst though the whole haith been as often promised as there is pounds in the sume due". Other partners were a Mr. Langstaff and Ralph Rowlings, and although it is not clear if Bathurst did come in, there were eventually six partners.

The land for the Cupuloe at Reels Head was purchased from Thomas Buckton for £9 and building work began late in 1700[23]. The mill was smelting by 1701; the mill manager was John Copperthwaite, a nephew of John Blackburne and Mr. Cross was the accountant.

John Blackburne was also a partner with Emmanuel Justice, a York merchant, in several mines and trials in Wharfedale, including Blue Groves on Buckden Gavel at Appletreewick, Kettlewell, Dawsey Rake, Hawkswick and on Horton Moor below Penyghent. Many local families were involved with these mines including the Luptons, Tennants, Alcocks, Christopher Falshaw and John Slinger.

By 1702, the Cupuloe was smelting ore from the Grinton mines owned by Reginald Marriott, Mr. Thompson's mines at Woodhall Greets in Wensleydale, which were described as the "New Trials", and from Copperthwaite where "White Ore" was obtained. The largest amount of ore, however, came from Buckden Gavel mines in which Justice and Blackburne were partners.

Ore for the Cupuloe seems to have arrived intermittently for, in July 1703, Copperthwaite notes "the workmen at Cupuloe are all idle for want of ore" but this was remedied the next month when they were smelting slags from Buckden Gavel.

Carriage of ore from Buckden cost £1-5s per fother and the smelters at the mill were paid 11/6d per 22 cwt fother for smelting. Coal for the Cupuloe came from several places including Theodore Bathurst's pits in the Bishoprick of Durham, from Scath Head and from Burton Park in Wensleydale where John Blackburne was in partnership with Simon Scrope of Danby in a pit[24]. Here, they had sunk a 23 fathom borehole and by 1703 were driving a level onto the shaft, the whole undertaking having a £7 per quarter pay bill.

Smelted lead from the Cupuloe was sent either to Stockton or York, and in 1703, the only year for which records have survived, the following amounts were sent. In June 96 pigs were sent first to the Hartforth Mill near Whashton, which was also a staging post for the Wharton Mines, and then to Mr. Cook the agent at Stockton. By September, another 140 pigs had been sent, the whole having a total weight of 13 tons – 11 cwt. Lead which was destined for York was sent first to Burton, which suggests that possibly Scrope was a partner in the Cupuloe, and by September a total of 1,284 pigs weighing 72 tons – 16 cwt had been sent by jagger to York.

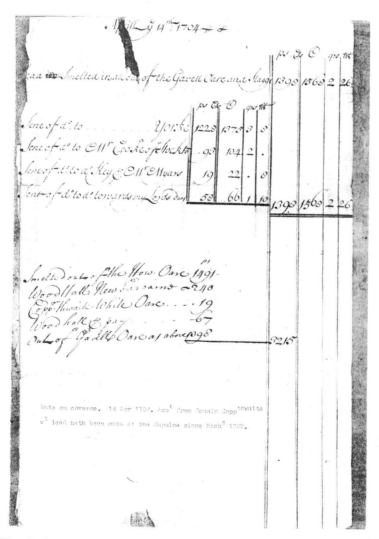

*Fig. 5. Account paper relating to the Cupuloe Smelt Mill, Marrick. (Brotherton Collection).*

*Fig. 6. and (next page) Fig. 7. Further examples of accounts relating to the Cupuloe Smelt Mill, Marrick.*

John Blackburne started, in September 1703, some trials on Leadmines Moss below Ingleborough. A lease was obtained from Mr. Bouche the landowner and three shallow shafts and an opencut on the vein raised some ore, the miners being paid £3-16s. The ore was then carried at a cost of 16s to the Cupuloe where a test smelt of this ore was made which cost £1-16s. A note at the bottom of the accounts for this venture sealed for ever any prospect of a lead industry in Chapel le Dale "it proved good ffor nothing"[25].

John Copperthwaite was complaining in December 1703 that due to Mr. Cross's irregular method of keeping accounts the ore carriers were being overpaid. Also in this month John Hutton, squire of Marske, proposed sending 40 horse load of ore from his mines in Kell pasture to the Cupuloe for trial. He also sent 40 to the Ellerton Mill and 40 to Lord Wharton's Mill and "which of these makes the best product must have the smelting it all".

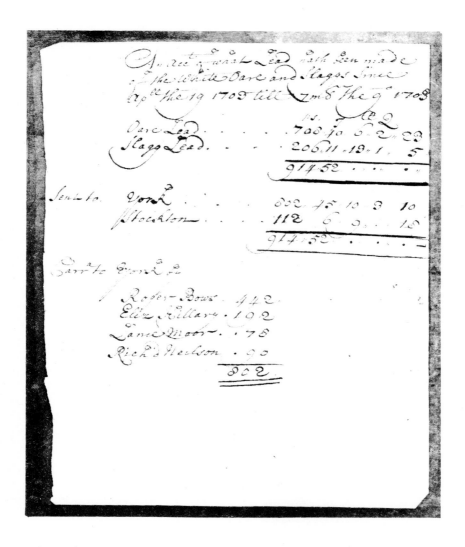

A letter from Copperthwaite in early 1704 mentions that Reuben Orton had dined with Sir Roger Beckwith of Walburn Hall at Mr. Stapelton's house at Clints, to make up the Cupuloe accounts and it is possible that Beckwith and Stapleton were partners in the Cupuloe.

Late in 1704, a series of legal wrangles began between John Blackburne and Emmanuel Justice. Basically, the partnership meant that Blackburne paid the workmen and Justice dealt with the lead sales but it transpires that poor John was being cheated on a grand scale.

Justice had enmeshed Blackburne in leases which he could ill afford, one at the Blue Groves, at Buckden, in 1696 when he was persuaded to take a sixth part with Justice, paying for the share and taking the money out of the mines without any receipt!!

As John Blackburne lived only nine miles from the mines, he spent a great deal of time visiting the mines for which he received no recompense. Justice would not concede to John selling goods to the miners or allow him a share in the hire of horses to the mines, both of which returned considerable profits. When he was offered 150 guineas for his 12th share in the Blue Groves, Justice refused to allow him to sell. So Blackburne was paying out money to the other partners, plus the running costs of the mines, and Squire was sending little or no money back from the lead sales which he had charge of.

The final straw came when Justice served a writ of ejectment on Blackburne and the other partners but as this was served on a Sunday it was not legally enforceable. Justice replied by calling a BarMoot Court, a consequence of which being that the partners and Blackburne were excluded from a share in the mines. He then proceeded to rip out as much ore as he could before a decision could be given, the ore being smelted at the Earl of Burlington's Buckden Mill[(26)].

John Blackburne was forced by debts, incurred in his mining ventures, to mortgage Fryerhead in 1705 to Robert Lowther. Whilst John had been away in London on business, his wife was persuaded by John Walker to lease Fryerhead lands to him for one year for a rental of £210. Walker did not pay any of this money and eventually Blackburne and Lowther were forced to take out a distress on the land.

Emmanuel Justice then took out a suit against Blackburne and Lowther for money owed to him by Blackburne but then dropped the case but payed costs only to Lowther. John then began legal proceedings to hold onto Fryerhead, but lacking sufficient funds to continue the case, he lost the estate to Lowther. It transpired that Walker had been persuaded by Lowther to take out a lease which he had no intention of paying for and then simply bankrupted Blackburne with legal costs, the whole affair being a strategy to get John out of Fryerhead. John and his wife were forced to return to live at Marrick Priory and their son John went to work as a clerk for his uncle in London.

In March 1706, John had to mortgage what was left of the Priory lands to Reginald Grayham for £1,260.

The mines in Grinton held by Reginald Marriott were the subject of a dispute in 1708 when Thomas Earl of Wharton contested the boundaries of the mines[(27)]. Marriott had been a Clerk in the Exchequor prior to 1702 and had taken the mines when he established they were concealed from the Crown. He married Dorothy, the daughter of Thomas Pulleine of Carleton Hall, Bedale, who was master of the Stud to King William and High Sheriff of Yorkshire in 1703. Marriott was M.P. for Weymouth.

The case was set to be heard in front of a special jury of Yorkshire Gentry on May the 8th but some days before the trial John Blackburne, who was to be jury foreman, was visited by Thomas Pulleine who offered to purchase on Marriott's behalf the Marrick Priory lands at the very high price of £2,300 if John would sway the jury members to view Marriott's case favourably when the bounderies were ridden and also to choose members of the jury whom he had the most influence with.

When in London prior to the hearing, Blackburne met with Reuben Orton in a coffee house, who told him that Mr. Dickinson, one of Marriott's agents, had made and signed on stamped paper an agreement to purchase the Cupuloe for £400 which Orton, as one of the partners, had accepted. Both these agreements were dependant on the outcome of the trial being to Marriott's benefit.

Lord Wharton had also been busy for he offered to obtain for John Blackburne a post in the Customs House in Liverpool.

The case was heard and found for Marriott but he then went back on his agreement with Blackburne over the purchase of the Priory estate. The agreement with Orton was honoured and he received the £400 although he avoided paying any of this money to the other partners in the Cupuloe.

In July 1709, a mob led by Thomas Pulleine violently broke into the Priory and took away several important documents and some household goods.

The Blackburne family were now much reduced in circumstances and survived on the goodness of relatives, staying for periods at houses in Ingleton, Lancaster and Preston. John Blackburne died soon after this last episode and his only survivor, John, obtained the post of steward to the Duke of Bolton in 1720.

*Plate II. An early photograph of the Level Houses at Hurst Crossroads. Note the horse which is pulling a hay sledge, which is only just descernable.*
*(Mr. R. Hillary).*

John Copperthwaite who was looking after the Priory for John Blackburne, wrote to him saying that Reuben Orton was involved with Thomas Waterhouse, a miner from Kettlewell, in some underhand dealings at the Cupuloe. John obtained a legal restraint against Waterhouse, in October 1723, from entering into any arrangements with Orton regarding the Cupuloe, but the following month Copperthwaite wrote saying he had been shown a letter from Waterhouse to Orton which contained an alleged discharge from trespass signed with Blackburne's signature.

It appears that Reuben Orton was busy pulling down the Cupuloe, which was ruinous by this time, and selling off the equipment, stone and timber for his own profit, without the permission of the various partners. John Blackburne approached Orton for a part of the money from the Cupuloe but Orton pretended his money was tied up in London and could not get there till a dispute between himself and Lord Powlett relating to when he was steward for Powlett was resolved.

John Blackburne moved down to London and took up practice in the Middle Temple. He wrote several letters to Reginald Marriott and his son, who were living in Parsons Green, for some restitution of the monies involved with the Cupuloe and Marrick Priory sales, but without success.

So the involvement of the Blackburne family came to an end when John sold the Priory site to James Piggott Ince and his son James Berkley Ince of Grays Inn prior to 1782. The site then passed to James's son, the Rev. Edward John Cumming Whittington-Ince of Bournemouth, rector of Warmingham.

## The Mines Under The Powlett Family

The boundary between Marrick and Marske was a constant source of dispute between the two lordships and to resolve these difficulties an agreement was signed on the 25th of June 1705 between Lord Powlett and John Hutton, Lord of the manor of Marske[28].

It was agreed that the boundary should run down the middle of Dales Beck although the wall on the east side of the Beck opposite the smelt mill was to be the property of William Powlett and he would be responsible for its upkeep. The main item in the agreement concerned lead waste washed down the beck from the dressings at the mill. Between the 11th of November and the 1st of May the workmen from the mill were to be allowed to reclaim this waste ore from both sides of the beck paying to John Hutton 20/- for every fother of lead reclaimed. There must have been one mill in operation at this time for the mill is referred to in the singular.

A lease for the Hurst mines was granted by Lord Powlett on the 21st of June 1718 to Samuel Mellor of Gyrn, Flints; John Halsall of St. Dunstans in the West, London; William Thompson, of Thames Street, London; and Thomas Jones of Pentreff, Flintshire. The lease was for 21 years beginning on 29th of November paying a duty of one seventh delivered at the mills ready for smelting[29].

By this time the hamlet of Hurst was beginning to grow as the mines expanded and Hurst Hall was built and occupied by Lord Powlett's steward John Cotesworth.

The lessees covenanted to employ no less than 147 miners, the lease being void if the mines were not worked for a period of two months. One provision in the lease being that Reuben Orton, John Copperthwaite, John Moreton or any other person discharged from service by Lord Powlett was not to be employed at the mines.

The partners were to share all profits in the following manner:- Mellor two shares, Halsall two shares, Jones and Thompson one share each, with all losses or charges to be born in the same proportion.

A disagreement soon arose between the partners as to who should be their agent at Hurst and they bound themselves for the sum of £200 to abide by the decision of two arbitrators, Solomon Wycliff of Dalton Travers and John Smith, with Christopher Clarke of Richmond as umpire. It was decided that the agent should be Thomas Kinnersley of Park Hall, Yorks, at an annual salary of £40 and the agreement was signed at the house of Mary Douglas in Fremington on the 21st of January 1719.

Annexed to the lease was a schedule of the workings, which indicates a quite extensive group of shafts and levels and which were mainly concentrated on the Golden Vein. The six upper levels were all used for drainage and ran in turn into the Low Level or Old Water Level which carried the water down to where it sank into a natural swallow in the faulted area near Washfold. Ore was raised via the shafts and some of the levels were also used as ventilation drifts.

Given below is a summary of the shafts and levels:-

## Shafts and Levels in Hurst Schedule, 1718

Shafts on Low Level which was 500 fathoms in length.

| | | |
|---|---|---|
| 1) | Shaft below Borehole Shaft | 12 fms |
| 2) | Borehole Shaft | 16½ fms |
| 3) | Wallnook Shaft | 24 fms |
| 4) | Cheatham Shaft where level turns onto vein | 18½ fms |
| 5) | Piggitt Shaft | 19½ fms |
| 6) | Smythy End or Smith Yard Shaft | 19 fms |
| 7) | Lady Shaft | 13 fms |
| 8) | Padley Shaft | 18½ fms |

Shafts on Black Level which was 38 fathoms in length.

| | | |
|---|---|---|
| 1) | Cocker Little Shaft | 14 fms |
| 2) | Cocker Deep Shaft | 22 fms |

Shafts on Slack Level which was 31 fathoms in length.

| | | |
|---|---|---|
| 1) | Cocker Deep Shaft | |

Both these levels met at Stoddart Sump Head on Cocker Deep Shaft.

Shafts on Gill level which was 143 fathoms in length and was described as dead but would need to be carried forward if the ore dipped as this was the lowest water level.

1)  Gill Shaft                                                    20½ fms
2)  Bromie Shaft                                                  20½ fms
3)  Down Shaft on Golden Vein                                     15 fms
4)  March Deep Shaft on Golden Vein                              19 fms

Shafts on Robinsons Level which was 30 fathoms in length and described as a wind level on the Golden Vein.

1)  First or Regnall March Shaft                                  18 fms
2)  Beard Shaft on Golden Vein                                    14 fms

There were two other levels on Bargh Side and connected with the main levels via the Smith Yard Shaft.

Lord William Powlett or the Duke of Bolton died in September 1729 and was succeeded by his son William who continued the family tradition as M.P. for Winchester and Lymington. Little information on the mines has survived for the next 70 years and therefore the narrative becomes sketchy.

The Minute Books of the London Lead Company record that it took a lease of the Hurst Mines on the 11th of June 1747 for 31 years paying one eighth duty[30]. The author has, however, been unable to find any independent confirmation that any work was done.

In 1757, on the 28th of May, William Powlett died and the estate decended to his daughter Annabel who married Rev. Richard Smyth of Itchen, Hants., in 1754. Their son William, born in 1758, had his name changed to Powlett in compliance with his grandfather's will and inherited the Marrick estate after his mother's death in 1781.

A map of the Marrick Estate made for William Powlett-Powlett in 1782 by Jackson, shows the mines were now a very extensive undertaking[31]. Several deep shafts had been sunk on Copperthwaite Vein and Sun Hush was working the east end of the Vein near the Hurst Road. South of the road, the Greenas Trials were being made to test the ground near Greenas Farm and down opposite the hamlet of Shaw the Shaw Level had been driven to connect with the two Shaw Shafts and Hillary Holes in order to try the Wallnook Vein.

The Jingle Pot Vein was being worked by several shafts and the Owlands Hard Crosscut tested the ground between the Jingle Pot and Grinton Dam Veins, but the main workings were on the Hurst Veins. The first level was driven onto these veins, the Nungate Level.

# CHAPTER 4

# THE MORLEY FAMILY. 1817 – 1895.

**W**ILLIAM POWLETT-POWLETT SOLD THE MANOR, MINES and demesnes of Marrick, plus the Rectory and Advowson of the Church of St. Andrew, in August 1817 to Josias Readshaw Morley of Beamsley Hall near Skipton. It was under this family that the mines were to reach their peak of production and eventual decline in 1890. When Josias purchased Marrick he was so encumbered with debts as to be nearly insolvent and a third estate at Addingham had to be sold off to keep himself afloat. He was pinning all his hopes of financial recovery on the mines at Hurst but the story of this family is one of continuous debt and effort to escape from its clutches.

Josias Morley was a partner in other Swaledale mines but his main holding was a three fourths share in the Ellerton Moor Mines, with Mathew Whitelock of Cogden Hall holding the other share. Here again he was in debt to the miners and tradesmen even though he had sold lead to the value of £16,000 and borrowed from Whitelock 1,600 pieces of lead at a value of £2,500[32].

*Plate III. An old picture of Washfold Hamlet and Hurst Board School. At top right are shown examples of very rare Bee Boles which served as a kind of beehive. Note also the steeply pitched thatched roof of the two storey house in the foreground.*
*(A. E. Bray O.B.E.).*

In February 1827, Josias Morley died and the estates – both heavily mortgaged – were left in trust to his son Francis who was 14 at the time. As trustees, Josias had appointed his brothers, John Readshaw Morley, merchant and Hanoverian Consul at Calais and Mathew Readshaw Morley of High Street, Southwark, merchant. They were allowed to lease the mines and appoint agents provided it was approved by two independant parties. The Beamsley estate had to be sold off to pay immediate debts and the trustees brought in Captain John Harland of Reeth to manage the Marrick estate and mines. He set about reorganising the mines and very soon repaid the debts to Whitelock, a debt of £4,000 on the Hurst Mines and eventually a total of £26,000 worth of debt was cleared by his efforts.

Soon after the debts at Ellerton were repaid, Miss Drax, who owned Ellerton estate, married a Mr. Sawyer who immediately set about recovering the mines, but before he could obtain an injunction from the Court of Chancery, it was found that the mines were worked out. One fact which did emerge during the preparation of the case was that Morley and Whitelock had never actually been granted a lease to work them!

At the Hurst Mines, the main workings were two deep whim shafts, the Middle Whim worked the Blindham, Golden and Cherry Veins, and Wellington Whim near the Fremington boundary worked the Blucher and Wellington Veins from the Low Rulleyway. The main level into this ground was the Hurst Horse Level started by Josias Morley soon after taking the manor, and driven towards the two whims with the aim of becoming the drawing level for the field.

A bargain book kindly loaned to the author provides a great deal of information about the period 1827 to 1850 and allows a good understanding of the development of the mines[33]. Unfortunately no production figures are known for this period.

John Harland's first priority was to organise movement of ore and new bargains were let for this purpose. George March undertook to lead all the ore from the Hurst mines to Marrick Smelt Mill at 1s-2d per bing and also took the bargain to draw, fill and team all the work at Hurst Horse Level at 1s-8d per draught of 8 wagons. Mathew Peacock took the drawing at Middle Whim at 2s-6d per draught which did not include filling or teaming and also took the drawing at Prys Whim for the same price. Thomas Hillary took the bargain for drawing the Wellington Whim at 3s-6d per draught, which price reflects the difference in depth. It is not clear if this refers to actually working the whim but it seems most likely.

Construction was started on new dressing floors, with a crushing mill, just to the south east of the Hurst Horse Level mouth, stone being brought by George March from Roan. The description of the stones for the wheel case are unusual; "the stones to be Scabled square with good beds and to be of large demention. The Heathers to be from 3 to 4 ft long and the Strickers to be 18" in the bed. This was the first central dressing floor to be constructed at Hurst, where previously all dressing was done at the various shafts spread about the field, making dressing very uneconomical.

*Plate IV. A view of Marrick High and Low Mills looking north. The tree at the side of the Low Mill is growing out of the wheelpit with ore lobbies to the side. These were built in 1863 when the mills were used for the last time.*

On the 1st of January 1828, the trustees of the late Josias Morley assigned a lease of the Hurst mining field to Robert Jaques of Easby House, Richmond; Edmund Alderson Knowles and John Birkbeck both of Low Row near Reeth; George Atkinson of Hagg Cottage; Richard McCollah of Reeth and Ottiwell Tomlin and Thomas Simpson both of Richmond; and at the request of the trustees John Harland took the last eighth share[34].

The lease was for 21 years paying 1/14th duty on good lead and the same on slag lead, delivered every four weeks or when one mark had been smelted. They were also to pay an annual rental of £800 in two half yearly equal portions. Seventy pickmen were to be constantly employed, half of whom had to be inhabitants of the manor of Marrick, and were to be paid half yearly on the 13th of May and the 23rd November. Within three months of the commencement of the lease a new trial was to be made down Wellington Whim of a 70 fms drive north and a 30 fms drive south with not less than 4 able bodied men in the bearing beds.

The above partners held a virtual monopoly by lease of most of the mining ground in Swaledale and Arkengarthdale and, although no lease has been found, it is almost certain they also worked the Fell End Mines. This is suggested when the Fell End Horse level was holed into down Wellington Whim in September 1827, and a bargain let to George March to carry ore from Fell End to Marrick Mill.

Plate V. Marrick High smelt mill ore hearths.

Plate VI. Marrick High smelt mill.

In March 1829, John Thompson and three partners took a bargain to drive the Green Hurst Horse Level at 9s per fathom and £8-10s for any ore they might find. This was an attempt to try in depth the Green Hurst Flots area. The Opencast Level was reopened in July but for what purpose is not clear. New bargains were let; Mathew Peacock took the filling, drawing and teaming at Wellington Whim at 5s per draught and at Hurst Horse Level at 1s-9d per draught, having to forfeit 6 weeks wages on failure to fulfill the contract[35]. Edward Hird took the dressing at the New Crushing Mill at 2s-5d per bing. George March took bargains to lead ore to Marrick Smelt Mill from Hurst Crushing Mill at 1s per bing, from Pryes Crushing Mill at 3s per bing and from Fell End at 2s-6d per bing. George Hillary and his son George took the filling, drawing and teaming at Middle and Pryes Whims at 4s-6d per draught. James Thompson undertook to deliver cinders from Tan Hill and William Gill Collieries to Marrick Smelt Mill at 4½d per bushel.

A new crushing mill was constructed at the mouth of Fell End Horse Level in July 1831, Mathew Peacock taking the bargain to get stones and wall the wheelcase, the walls being 3 ft broad and covered with "throughs each 3ft in height, at 1s-2d per yard". By November 1831, Thomas Alderson, who was the main driving contractor in the Fell End Horse Level was through into the Hurst ground.

Benjamin Brown began sinking a shaft near Marrick Lane in 1833 to try the junction of the Old Smeltings Vein and Marrick Great Vein, and ten years later the Marrick Moor Horse Level also tried this area.

Francis Morley, the heir of Josias came of age in 1834 and two years later married Miss Charlotte Chaytor, eldest daughter of John Clervaux Chaytor of Spennithorne Hall. Their son Francis was born in November of the same year. Francis was a J.P. and a Captain in the North Yorkshire Regiment.

The northern limits of the manor of Marrick are bounded by Moresdale Ridge and on January 4th 1836 the Moresdale Ridge Level was started by George March with the aim of cutting the Moresdale Great Vein near March's Shaft. To ensure constant working in this remote setting a penalty clause was inserted in the contract whereby the price of the last 12 fms driven was to be held back till the following pay and would be forfeit on failure to comply with the bargain agreement. Four men were to be constantly employed and the rise of the level sole to be not more than ¼" per fathom. The initial price per fathom was 36s, but had to be raised as the ground became more unstable, till £5 per fathom was reached. In 1844, another level was started on the north side of the Ridge known as Porter Level, and was driven south to cut the Sun Vein and unusually the level sole had to be paved.

The most significant development at Hurst was started on June 5th 1837 when Joseph Hawkin and three partners took a bargain to drive the Queens Level. This level was developed by two main drives, Queens Sun crosscut on the Cleminson and Redshaft Veins and Queens North crosscut on the Wellington and Golden Veins. From the North crosscut Browns Sump eventually connected with the Old Water Level and from Browns Low Rulleyway the lower beds could be worked. (See section).

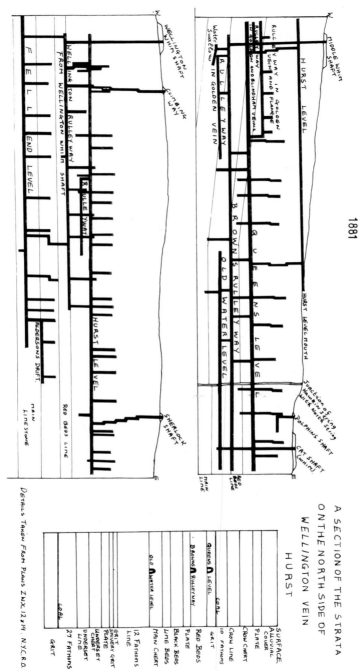

Fig. 8. Sections on the workings at Cat Shaft and Wellington Whim.

40

The lease of 1828 lasted for 14 years when a disagreement over Francis Morley's liability to pay his own Income Tax out of the proceeds of the mines caused the lease to be terminated. Morley also dismissed John Harland and attempted to work the mines on his own behalf. Despite having to pay no duty or dead rent he succeeded in getting himself into debt with the Stapleton Bank in Richmond to the sum of £1,800.

Within two years, Morley was forced to apologise to John Harland and ask him to take over the running of the mines once again, and very soon the debts to Stapletons Bank was reduced.

Morley then asked his uncle, William Morley in London to try and form a company to work the mines and a Percival Johnson* was sent up to make a survey and report[36]. Through his partner Mr. Murray, Johnson introduced Francis to Mr. Peter Stainsby, who was managing director to several mines in the south-west of England. This attempt to form a company failed but soon after, John Harland was introduced by George Allinson of Darlington to a Mr. Gillan of London and Thomas Brown of Tudhoe Co. Durham, who, with Murray and himself, formed a company to work the mines in 1844.

Gillan and Brown soon withdrew from the partnership, handing their shares to John Harland who then sold one share to Mr. Brown Simpson of Richmond. Murray then found himself in financial difficulties and sold his share to Brown Simpson, thus Harland and Simpson became the major shareholders.

They gained little financially from the mines but a considerable income went to Morley in Duty Lead and Ore. In 1852, the lessees were approached for a quantity of unsmelted lead ore and it was found to be to the advantage of both lessee and lessor that instead of smelting the ore themselves it should be sold as ore and a money duty paid instead. The main advantage being that the ore could be sold monthly instead of holding pig lead for six or nine months which also entailed a loss of interest and often of value.

During this period, Francis Morley had been forced to adopt all sorts of devices to fend off the various holders of mortgages on the estate but, despite the vigorous efforts of John Harland to keep him solvent, Francis was forced, in 1848, to flee the country and live with his uncle in Calais.

John Harland agreed to become assignee of Morley's Real and Personal estate and Simpson paid £252 interest on a £20,000 mortgage of the estate to Mr. Dunn of Newcastle out of his own pocket and Morley was able to return to England. Other debtors agreed to wait for payment out of surplus rents from the estate after living expenses for the Morley family were deducted.

Francis Morley died on the 3rd of August 1854 but when John Harland went to attend the funeral on the 10th he was met by hostile and sinister looks from the family and two days later was informed that Christopher Lonsdale Bradley had been appointed as estate and mine manager and that his services were no longer required.

---

*Percival Norton Johnson. A pioneer metallurgist who founded the well known business Johnson, Matthey & Co. Ltd. Johnson had many interests in Cornwall — particularly his famed Tamar Silver Lead Mining Company. Stainsby often appeared as a co-director in these enterprises. (Ed.)

*Plate VII. Marrick Low Mill ore hearths.*

Soon after the death of Francis, his wife was appointed Administrix and Mr. Robson of Robson and Wood, Drapers of Richmond, was persuaded to take out a friendly bill against Mrs. Morley. The various creditors were called to show proof of debt but on offering this proof the debts were declared void due to the Statue of Limitations Act and, therefore, the creditors received nothing. Mrs. Morley and Mr. William Saunders of Wennington Hall near Lancaster, the husband of the late Francis Morley's sister, then brought an action against John Harland for £16,000. So it came about that John Harland, who had dedicated 28 years of his life saving the Morley family from beggary, was reviled and abused in court and as a finale was expected to pay them a sum of £16,000. Fortunately this case was never fully proceeded with.

The outcome of all this legal wrangling was that all the debts and mortgages which Josias and Francis contracted prior to the Fraud Act of 1831/2 were void and, therefore, it transpires that the Marrick estate was purchased with borrowed money of which not a penny needed to be repayed.

After the death of Francis Morley the estate passed to his son Francis who, being under age, had appointed as his guardians John Clervaux Chaytor, A. H. Darcy and his mother. Harland and Simpson continued to work the mines although Bradley insisted they should go back to paying the duty in smelted lead which went against the agreement made in 1852. From the commencement of the lease of 1827, all timber from the Marrick estate was to be sent to the Hurst mines but after Morley's death in 1854, when Bradley took over the running of the mines, with the exception of small amounts sent to the Grinton mines, the bulk of timber was sold to other mining companies, many of which Bradley had an interest in and none sent to the Hurst Mines[37].

42

Prior to his death in 1854, Francis Morley had taken a lease from the Crown of the Whitaside mines and held a one fourth share; he also held a fourth share in the Summer Lodge Mine and a third share in Grinton Mines. These shares were all put up for sale on February 6th 1857 on the orders of the Court of Chancery, presumably to go some way to pay off the debts of Francis Morley[38]. After this sale Francis Morley went to Corfu only returning in 1861.

*Plate VIII (left).*
*Cat Shaft Chimney, Hurst.*
*Built in 1883.*

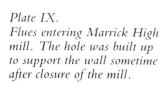

*Plate IX.*
*Flues entering Marrick High*
*mill. The hole was built up*
*to support the wall sometime*
*after closure of the mill.*

On his return, a fresh lease of the mines was drawn up with a new company headed by George Leeman, a York solicitor, an M.P. and three times Lord Mayor of that city, who also had interests in North Yorkshire ironstone mines. The other partners were William Fox Clarke of York, C. L. Bradley of Richmond, Thomas Jackson of Eltham Park, Kent; Thomas Jackson junior of Eltham Park; Alfred William Bean of Shooters Hill, Kent; and James Gow of Fowlers Park, Kent. The new lease was to run for 21 years starting on January 1st 1861 yielding one twentieth of all slag lead and one twentieth of all good lead delivered at the ore house or smelt mills ready for smelting. There was also a dead or certain annual rent of £200 and the lessees reserved the right to pay the 1/20th after being smelted in which case the lessor was to pay or allow on account 20/- per ton. The lessors were to pay all taxes etc and standard weights were to be used for weighing off the pigs, which from time to time were to be tested against the standard weights used at Richmond Market.

There were to be no less than 50 pickmen employed and the lessees were to continue driving two levels which were in the course of construction at this time. Pryes Level, started in 1859, was 180 fathoms in length, being driven to cut the vein at East Close Shaft, and Porter Level, driven south from Moresdale Beck, and 230 fathoms in length.

The lessors were to pay as a goodwill payment £500 within one month of signing the lease and another £500 in two parts at six montly intervals. Coal, which was known to be present at Hurst, was excepted from the lease. A row of new houses were built for the miners at this time and to this day are known as Shiny Row.

Francis Morley obtained a commission as an officer in the 1st Battalion, 3rd Regiment of Foot or the "Buffs" in 1863 leaving Lonsdale Bradley in charge of the mines and estates. Leeman & Co., trading as the Hurst Mining Company, had Robert Daykin as their main agent and Robert Metcalfe as his assistant. George Chalder, who had been agent at Hurst for 66 years, died in 1859 aged 88.

# CHAPTER 5

## THE HURST MINING COMPANY. 1861 – 1880.

THE FIRST PRIORITY OF THE NEW COMPANY WAS TO refurbish the mills to cope with the expected rise in production. They found that the High Mill was beyond use so all their efforts were concentrated on the Low Mill, and by building a flue up to the chimney at the High Mill would be able to reclaim some of the fume, or lead soot.

In November 1862, John Hillary began cutting a new wheel-case and in December Robert Thompson of Fremington with 4 horses, two wagons and two men began hauling a 20ft diameter, 39 inch breast water wheel, plus machinery which cost £55, from the Lane End Mines at the head of Swaledale for use at the Low Mill.

James Flint, Ironmaster, of the Royal Foundry in Richmond supplied, in March 1863, two metal coupling boxes, one cast iron shaft weighing 2 cwt at a cost of £2-3-1½d. At each end of the shaft journals were cut, one 7" x 4½" and one 6 x 4½", and one brass bush weighing 3lbs 1oz was also supplied.

William Allinson of Reeth had to reinforce the mill wall to take the weight of the wheel and Thomas Coates cut and walled the gutter, put in a sluice and built posts to carry the launder for the wheel in April. He also took slates from

*Plate X. Pryes Mine shop or office and portal of Pryes Level.*

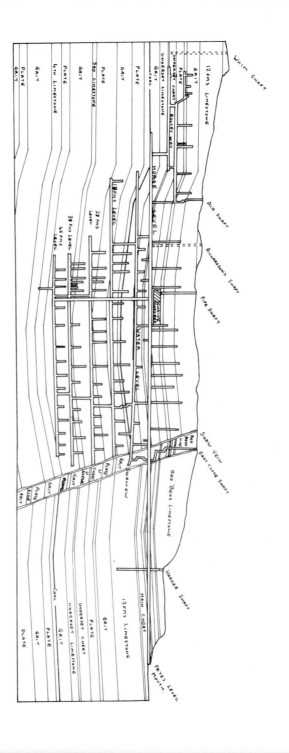

Fig. 9. Section of Pryes Level showing strata on north side of Pryes Vein. 1880.

the High Coals House for an ore lobby at the mill, paved the wheel case, slated the roof of the mill and set the corbels and water tubbing which had been brought from Stainton Quarry.

Thomas Coates of Stelling began cutting the earth for the new flue up to the High Mill in August and William Allinson took stone from the High Mill chimney to build the sides of the flue. Slates for the flue top were brought from Stainton Quarry, 55 yards at 11d per flag.

Thomas Coates then layed clay along the sides of the flue and covered the whole with soil. The windows and doors in the High Mill were sealed, which suggests that some form of condenser might have been fitted up in the High Mill. Daykin and Metcalf were each paid £10 for supervising this work. A slag hearth must have gone into production at the Low Mill at this time for slag lead now feature in the returns.

The Kinnaird Commission presented its report on British Mines in 1863 and the Hurst Mines were visited by its Inspector, Charles Twite, in January[39].

Pryes Mine, which worked the greatest depth at Hurst, was by this time 240 fathoms from the mouth, driven in plate and 9ft x 7ft, and 8 men were employed here working four shifts of six hours duration. The Inspector visited a drift 8 fathoms below the main level horizon which was driven in Plate and used as a water level. The air was so foul that candles had to be held upside down in order to keep them alight. One of the Workmen said he burned five candles per six hour shift and the bad air affected his breathing and caused headaches.

*Plate XI. Bouse teams at Pryes Mine.*

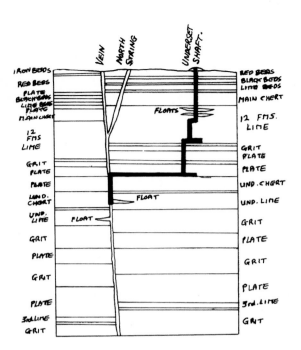

*Fig. 10.*
*Section at*
*Underset Shaft on*
*the Copperthwaite*
*Level. 1880.*

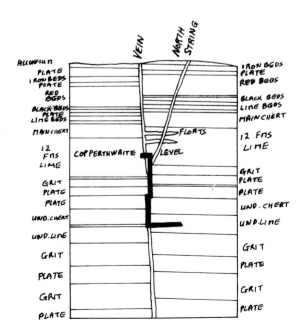

*Fig. 11.*
*Section at*
*Kendal's sump on*
*the Copperthwaite*
*Level. 1880.*

The main level on the Hurst Mines was Queens Level which was about a mile in length at this date. Six men, two per shift, were driving a drift 12 fms above the main level which was ventilated by a draught going through the rise to a higher level which communicated with the surface, the air being carried to the forehead by airpipes.

Hurst Horse Level was the highest level on the field, about fifty fathoms above Queens, which worked the upper beds and was also about a mile in length heading towards the Fell End Mines on Fremington Edge.

Copperthwaite Level to the south of the main Hurst mines was about ¾ of a mile in length with the vein being stoped away by about 30 men, ventilation being provided by air shafts. Three trial levels were being driven with four men in each: Marrick Moor Level, Marrick High and Low Levels.

Robert Daykin, aged 48, was examined when the Commission visited Reeth in March 1863. He testified there were 67 pickmen employed on the whole field with some women on the various dressing floors which were scattered about the field and open to the elements.

*Plate XII. Bouse teams at Copperthwaite. These have been obliterated since this picture was taken.*

Pryes Mine was a poor mine at this time with 30 men working day and night shifts. Drainage at Pryes was by the Water Level 8 fms below the main level, which ran into a natural swallow in the limestone and could take 140 gallons per minute in bad weather. This connected with the East Close Shaft and an air drift, which ran parallel with the main level, provided an air circuit aided by the water running away down the swallow. When the Inspector had visited the mine in January the swallow had been overset with water which prevented the air circuit working – thus causing the bad air – and as soon as the wa⸱

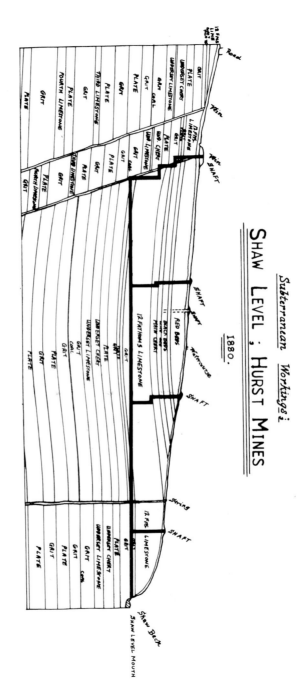

Fig. 12. Section through strata at Shaw Level, Hurst Mines. 1880.

50

abated the air current resumed. Also employed for ventilation purposes were two "windy kings", one worked by water and the other by a boy and the air was conveyed to the working places by wooden trunking boxes 6" by 4".

The men were payed monthly and had to pay for powder, tools and drawing and also had to purchase their candles from the company at 8/- per dozen, a dozen costing the company 5/6d.

Francis Morley, now a Major, returned to England in April 1866 and very soon became dissillusioned with the way Bradley had been running the mines for him. He appointed H.T. Robinson of Leyburn as his new estate manager and William Anthony Waggett of Marrick as his local agent. A list was drawn up of the various discrepancies made in the accounts by Bradley since 1858[40]. Vouchers were missing, there were no vouchers for his wages, duty lead was charged for smelting when it was under the dead rent of £200, and the repairs to the smelt mill, which came to £172-12-7d, Bradley had never received authorization to commence.

Morley was so disturbed by these irregularities that he withdrew from the 1861 lease and ordered a new one drawn up. This was to run for 21 years from January 1st 1867 for 21 years, paying one tenth duty but Leemen & Co asked for an extended lease to run from January 1st 1868, the one tenth duty to be extended for seven years with the duty from 1866 being arbitrated upon[41]. It would be optional whether the lessor took the machinery at the end of the lease and 80 pickmen were to be constantly employed.

The lessees were to be allowed to sell unsmelted ore and had the option if they thought best to smelt part into lead and sell the rest as ore but the lessor must not be charged with the expense of smelting his duty lead but receive the duty whether in lead or ore, free of all charges, and the duty ore to be carried to Richmond free of charge. Buildings and land at Hurst could be leased by the company for 21 years but the Public House, Gamekeeper's House and land and Middletons Farm were not to be let. It was part of the tenancy agreements at Hurst that tenants must work at no other mines than those of the Hurst Mining Company.

One particularly interesting clause to be inserted in the new lease was that any man convicted of an offence by a magistrate was to be instantly dismissed by the compay and this rule was to be stringently enforced on account of the damage done to the grouse shooting on the nearby moors.

Major Morley calculated the monies owing from the 1/10th duty plus other monies thus:-

The £1,000 advanced to Major Morley to form part of the give and take on the old lease at 5% p.a. to 31st Dec 1866 i.e. the £1,000 plus interest at 5% p.a. from 1861 - 1866, plus the difference paid by the company to make up the minimum duty of £200 p.a. from 1861 - 1865, in 1866 the duty exceeded £200, at 1/20th is equal to £1,000 + £300 + £287-3-8d or £1,587-3-8d. The duty at 1/10th from 1861 - 1866 inclusive is as follows:-

|  | £ | s | d |
|---|---|---|---|
| 1861 at 1/10th | 343 | 12 | 04 |
| 1862 at 1/10th | 222 | 02 | 08 |
| 1863 at 1/10th | 286 | 04 | 00 |
| 1864 at 1/10th | 214 | 09 | 00 |
| 1865 at 1/10th | 358 | 12 | 08 |
| 1866 at 1/10th | 533 | 12 | 00 |
|  | £1958 | 12 | 08 |

The £1,000 + interest 5% p.a. + difference in cash to complete £200 p.a. = £1,587-7-8d.

Difference in Morley's favour = £371-9s.

Repairs at Smelt Mill not allowed by lease but charged in accounts by C.L. Bradley without authority = £200

Total in Major Morley's favour to 31st December 1866 = £571-9s.

The duty in 1867 at 1/10th was about £500.

In a letter to H. T. Robinson written in April 1867, Morley says that the proposed lease could not be found and that he should "get the weight of all the lead sent to Richmond since Bradley & Co had the mines and the names of the people who have purchased the ore"[42]. "Waggett will have to keep a sharp look out on the lead ore or we may be done yet". "Would it be possible for the mining agents to shift the heaps of ore in such a manner that Waggett could not tell to a certainty which had been weighed and which had not?" The most telling phrase appears at the end of this letter "I think that Bradley's star is on the wane".

The counterparts of the new lease continued to be passed back and forth between the solicitors for the respective parties. Leeman & Co did not want to accept Morley's 1/10th duty and the length of time of the new lease, and preferred a 1/10th money payment of the net produce of sales instead of a render in kind.

On February 6th 1868, Leeman wrote to Robinson at Leyburn that he objected most strongly to paying for all repairs to the smelt mills as well as consenting to carry the 1/10th per year back to 1866, "What have my colleagues and myself to do with the private correspondance between Major Morley and Mr. Bradley as his land agent? I object to our being responsible for Bradley's liabilities to Morley". The new lease was finally signed by all parties in London on the 26th of February 1868.

A letter sent to Robinson in 1868 promised to open up a new era in Swaledale when Mr. Tomlin of Richmond wrote to him regarding the proposed railway to Reeth from Richmond passing through Morley's land at Applegarth Low Wood and how the Major might view this proposal.

Major Morley embarked for Egypt in April with his regiment bound for service in India.

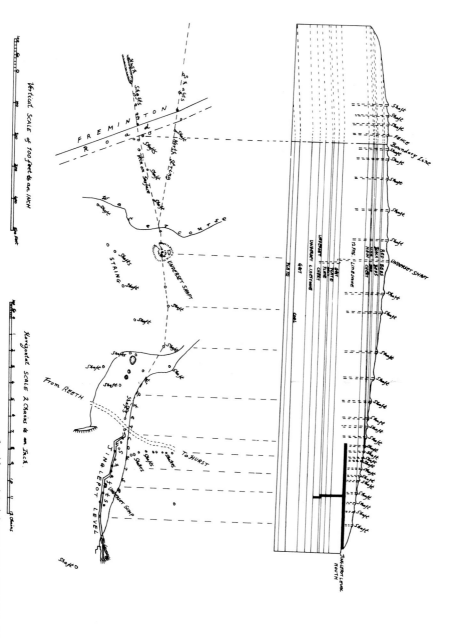

Fig. 13. Plan and section of the workings at Jinglepot Level, Hurst Mines, 1880.

Vertical Scale of 100 feet to an Inch

Horizontal Scale 2 Chains to an Inch

Traced from original plan ZUK15. Sketch by North Yorks. County Records Office.

53

Lonsdale Bradley finally retired as manager of the Hurst Mining Co. on June 6th 1868 and was replaced by Ralph Metcalfe with James March as his assistant. Robert Daykin had left Hurst in December 1867 and gone to work in Cumberland.

That was not the last to be heard from Bradley for, in September, Waggett notified Robinson that Bradley had written to James March and asked him to send the Mining Co's account books secretly to him in London. Whatever Bradley was planning came to nought and he went to manage an estate somewhere in the Midlands near the Welsh Border.

Waggett managed to get £500 from the company in December and Morley wrote in reply "we must not let them get into arrears again. I think they are well rid of Lonsdale Bradley". He was also asked by Morley to get the assistance of Ralph Metcalfe and canvas the people of Hurst and Marrick to vote for Duncombe and Millbank in the forthcoming elections. Metcalfe replied that the tenants under the company would of course comply with this request.

Major Morley ordered that £3 be contributed towards a fund being set up for the family of John Frankland, aged 34, who was killed in the Hurst mines sometime in 1868. He lived in Shiny Row and left a widow Lydia and four children.

Another letter from Morley written in December mentions for the first time the coal deposits at Roan Head. He says he would rather have a duty than yearly rental and if the mining company make a satisfactory offer then he would allow them to work it. "I cannot think of letting them have it on a long lease and on no account would I agree for the coal being used for any other purposes than burning lime and smelting lead. Should the village people burn it in their houses I will have the place shut up at once." The value of the coal would have to be calculated on the comparison of prices and the quality of the coal at Richmond, including carriage to Hurst.

In reply to the earlier enquiry as to his feelings on a railway up Swaledale, he asked that any proposed station for Marrick be at Ellerholme and "I shall be obliged if you oppose the scheme as hard as you can in order to force up the compensation". This scheme never came to fruition.

Morley wrote to Waggett in April 1869 saying "An eye must be kept on C. L. Bradley and when he seems in a position to pay the money which he owes he must be looked up, in the meantime you may as well keep him in mind of the amount of his debts".

Waggett wrote in June 1869 that he had had a favourable report on the mines and if the water could be kept down at Pryes so the men can work then a great deal of ore could be raised from the depth now reached; this ore was also of a better quality than that nearer the surface. Metcalfe, the H.M.Co. agent, said that they would be obliged to have a steam engine before winter as the present one could not both draw waste and pump water. The matter of the coals had been discussed and it was thought to be best for both parties if the coals were worked as they would be needed for the proposed steam engine. A hydraulic engine must have been installed under Bradley's direction for he used this type of engine at Stonesdale and Blakethwaite which he also leased and managed, and it helps to explain Leeman's anxiety to keep the lease despite the extra duty payments.

A total of 97 bings had been raised since December 1868 from Pryes Mine and it seems the company were concentrating on Pryes at this time. Morley, however, was not satisfied for in August he wrote "I do not think the mining company are working the field in an energetic manner, I hear of no new trials being made and I think there are several that should be attempted. I shall not let the company work the coals unless they sink a shaft and cut the Pryes Vein in the neighbourhood of the High Public House, if I remember rightly there is a shaft somewhere about there above the vein named Cat Shaft".

Waggett visited, with Metcalfe in September 1869, the lower workings in Pryes which he thought would bear a fair quantity of ore but of a coarse nature. There was some doubt that the vein in the west forehead would bear so far west in the present sinking as it did in the last one. Since July 1869 there had been sent from the mines 352½ bings of grove ore, 44⅜th bings of waste ore and 120 pieces of lead weighed.

Early in 1870, the matter of the money owing to Morley for the smelt mill repairs was again raised with the company, who replied that they were unable to meet the account at present. Morley proposed that if he laid out £200 on driving a level on the Marrick side of the estate would the company be prepared to invest a similar amount. It is not known exactly where this proposed level was to be but it could well have been intended to try some of the veins which run through Marrick Village.

Writing to Waggett from India in July 1870, Morley asked if he had heard any more about Leeman's intentions regarding the mines. "If the company intend giving up the mines then a competent man must be engaged to survey the mines and see if they are in good condition. If Mr. Leeman's mind is running on a lower duty than one tenth then we may as well dispel the illusion at once".

By July 1870, 900 bings of grove ore and 112⅜ bings of waste ore had been sold.

Another letter from Morley to Waggett in July 1870 voiced his dissatisfaction with the company. "I am sorry to hear Mr. Leeman is not much better for his sojourn in Germany. He may make his mind easy on one point and that is under any circumstances I do not intend to reduce the Royalty, and should the Co. be inclined to give up the mines we must try and let them to another company on the same terms".

The grouse moors at Hurst were let in 1870 to Mr. Gilpin Brown who held the neighbouring estate of Arkengarthdale. The cost of new boundary stones were to be shared between the two owners with their initials and date on respective sides.

In August of 1870, there were droughty conditions and Waggett noted there was insufficient water for the Pryes Engine to pump the water and draw the work as well. James March wrote on behalf of the company that on account of the scarcity of water for some time they had been unable to work at Pryes and had only dressed 25 bings of ore for the last month.

The smelt mill door was forced open in February 1871 and the Scale Balk stolen. The police were investigating and the Balk was returned a week later.

James March wrote to Morley in February 1872 that the company were paying the Royalty in cash but were obliged to take bills at three months for their lead ore sales so there was a week or ten days before the last bill became due which accounted for the company's inability to make the payments in full and on time.

Morley wrote to Waggett in July 1872 again expressing his unhappiness with the way in which the mines were being worked. "I think it would be a good thing if they would give them up either of their own accord or by pressure and then we could set up a Limited Liability Company".

The payment for the smelt mill repairs due since 1868 was finally settled in December 1872 when Morley accepted £100.

Early in 1873, Anthony Waggett was sent to the Tan Hill coal pits to get some experience in coal mining and on his return a trail was begun at Roan Head at a cost of £15. The coal was advertised to be let in the *Yorkshire, Ripon & Richmond Chronicle*. The trial was continued in the summer of 1874 but seems to have been unsuccessful.

In January 1874, Francis Morley was forced by legacies incurred under the terms of his grandfather's will, and never cleared by his father, to take out a mortgage of £8,000 on the Marrick estate. Payments of £3,000 each were due to Major Morley's brother Clervaux Darcy Chaytor of Spennithorne Hall, his sister Mary and Dorothy, who was married to William Allen Francis Saunders of Wennington Hall near Lancaster, Francis having received the manor, mines and shares in Surrender, Whitaside, Ellerton Moor and Grinton. The money was loaned by Francis Riddell of Cheeseburn Grange, Northumberland and Edward Leadbitter of Newcastle upon Tyne.

Ore production at the Mines began to decline in 1876 and the following year an outside mining agent, Thomas Davidson, was brought in to view the mines and write reports for Morley and Leeman.

# CHAPTER 6

# THE YORKSHIRE LEAD MINING COMPANY. 1881 - 1890.

THE HURST MINING COMPANY WERE, BY 1880, PAYING THE dead rent of £500 and Waggett was working the mines on a small scale. This situation continued till April 26th 1881 when Faithfull Cookson, who was involved with the Lane End/Keldside Mines at the head of Swaledale, took a six month exploratory lease of the mines.

In May 1881, George Robinson of Kettleness, Cleveland, made an inspection of the mines on behalf of Cookson. He advised sinking a trial shaft near the High Public House and strongly recommended that a full lease be taken for the Hurst Mines.

The Reeth Poor Law Union Assessment Committee put the Hurst mines on the Parish valuation list at £200 and the grouse shooting at £400 which says a great deal for the value of the mines at this time.

Waggett sent 11½ tons of ore and 2 tons of waste ore, which the miners had dressed on their own account, to be smelted at Middleton in Teesdale in June, and Bainbridge, the agent for the Middleton Mining Company, sent a cheque for this ore paying £8-2-6d per ton.

The mines at Hurst were visited in July by Cookson and Sir Francis Knowles and Waggett informed Morley that they seemed pleased with the undertaking. It was proposed to put an engine down at Cat Shaft and clear the Old Water Level, which during Josias Morley's time, had been extended as far as Cat Shaft and when reopened would drain all the top ground.

When Metcalfe went to see his old employers in York about the mine plant, he was told not to make any arrangements regarding the plant but returned with a cheque for £578-3-7d to pay off some of the company's arrears.

Waggett noted in a letter to Morley in July 1881, that there could be problems in getting the plant removed peacably for some time and it may be necessary to get an eviction notice against them. This letter also contains an interesting paragraph on the new company, "As the new lessees of the mines have neither plant nor tools of their own they have to borrow from the old company and as some of the men they are employing do not seem to be Mr. Metcalfe's sort, and as these men have been in the habit of taking things without asking the Agent's consent they appear not to get on amicably together".

Cookson signed the new lease on October 6th 1881. It was to run for 21 years with the Royalty payments divided into three seven year parts. For the first seven years a Royalty of one twentieth, for the second seven years one sixteenth and the final seven years one fourteenth, plus a dead rent of £100 per annum and a yearly payment of £5 for the coal.

Faithfull Cookson transferred his right to this lease on February 4th 1882 when a new company, the Yorkshire Lead Mines Ltd., was set up to work the Hurst Mines. The company had a share capital of £65,000 and the following each held one share; T. M. Roby, Wimbledon, retired captain; A. North, Kingsbury, accountant; E. G. Fellowe, 3-4 Great Winchester Street Buildings, broker; F. G. Fellowe, 3 Budge Row, no occupation; R. A. Burnell, Shepherds Bush, commission merchant; J. E. Harding, Camberwell, accountant; A. Garrett, Walworth, civil engineer. These subscribers were to determine the first seven directors.

A mining engineer, W. H. Hosking, was appointed to make a survey of the mines and to oversee their development with a Cornishman, John Retallick as the resident agent.

The dressing plant owned by the old company was put up for sale in June 1882 and purchased by Mr. Robert Richards, iron merchant of Sunderland[43].

By October 1882, the Old Water Level had been cleared for a distance of 400 fathoms towards Cat Shaft and six other shafts had also been cleared and secured for ventilation purposes. Cat Shaft itself was being timbered and enlarged to 8ft by 5½ft. and was 24 fms. down with 16 to go in order to reach the Water Level. Coal had been found in the shaft in a 14" seam which, fortunately, was found to be of excellent quality and ideal for the intended engine on Cat Shaft and could be delivered to the engine at 5/6d per ton[44].

The engine installed on Cat Shaft was an 18" high pressure horizontal engine to be used for pumping and winding and was in work by November 1883. The coal seam was improving and providing a plentiful supply both for the engine and the miners at a nominal cost. The Old Water Level was now cleared up to Cat Shaft, the final 160 fathoms from Browns Sump to Cat Shaft being driven on one of the Hawkins Strings which was 2 to 3ft wide carrying a good 6" leader of solid galena, expected to give six tons of metal per fathom. In the area of Cat Shaft were six veins which had not been fully exploited by the old man below the Old Water Level and expectations of rich strikes raised everyones' hopes. From the base of the shaft a cross cut south was into the 3ft wide Gutter String and 15fms further on Redshaft Vein had been cut, at which point the old man workings had run, making it necessary to redrive the cross cut. In the north cross cut from the shaft base another of the Hawkins Strings had been cut and 25fms further north lay the Woodgarth Vein[45].

The engine was raising the ore stuff to Queens Level for tramming out, the deads being raised to surface for dumping. As there was little water it had not been necessary to use the engine for pumping. Unfortunately the dressing machinery was not ready so they were unable to make any returns at that time.

The optimism engendered by the progress being made at the mines was not being reciprocated by the shareholders. At a special meeting called on May 8th 1884, the shareholders had allowed the directors to borrow on mortgage debentures £3,500 but only a small amount of this was raised, which at least enabled them to purchase the necessary washing and dressing plant, but did not leave sufficient funds to erect this machinery[46].

Ore was being raised from the two south veins and there was 50 tons ready for dressing, valued at £300.

At another special meeting held in January 1885, the directors appealed once more to the shareholders to provide funds to enable them to sink Cat Shaft a further 5 fms. and drive north to cut three known strong veins. A sum of £17,000 would be sufficient to accomplish this work and would put the mines

*Plate XIII. Brown's Engine shaft. Foundation for boiler in foreground and chimney above. Built in October 1887.*

on a sound base for expansion and produce considerable profits. If the money was not forthcoming then it might necessitate a voluntary or compulsory winding up of the company.

This money was provided, the main amount coming from Mr. Townsend Kirkwood, a lead smelter, who by June 1885, was taking personal control of the mines and machinery to enable regular supplies to be sent to Newcastle via Richmond where the ore was much in demand. Deliveries were expected to commence in July at an anticipated rate of 100 to 500 tons per month[47].

The mines at this time were held on a nominal rent of £100 per annum merging into a Royalty of one sixteenth and the ore could be dressed and sent to market at £4-10s per ton, leaving the shareholders a profit of £4 per ton at extant prices. Shares in the company were £1 fully paid up and 10s to 12/6d had been called by 1885.

With the necessary funds coming in, a new air of optimism ran through the mines. Another engine, a 14" high pressure horizontal, working two skips which held half a ton apiece, was installed and working by July 1885 to save using the pumping engine in a dual role. The engineers were working till dark every night in order to get the dressing machinery ready[48].

Strangely, reports on the mines, which had appeared regularly in the *Mining Journal* now ceased and letters from shareholders expressing concern about this secrecy were published. This had no effect till September 1886, when a report appeared saying that large quantities of high grade ore had been found and which, unusually for Yorkshire, was very rich in silver. There were now 150 men employed and the shares which had been depressed rose several shillings[49].

In February 1887, a miraculous escape occurred when Thomas Pounder, aged 26, of Ivelet near Gunnerside, slipped whilst descending a ladder and fell to the bottom of a shaft. When reached by other miners, blood was oozing from his nose and ears and he had several bodily injuries. He was raised from the mine and carried home where he recovered after several months. What made the accident worse was that it happened on the day prior to his wedding[50].

At the A.G.M. held at the company's offices in Gracechurch Street, London, on April the 9th 1887, the Chairman declared a profit of £2,170-8-11d. This was sufficient to pay a dividend of 9% after writing off £845 for depreciation of plant and money used in development, but he recommended that this dividend be witheld in order to pay monies due to the vendors for shares on the formation of the company. The retiring director Dr. McClure was re-elected[51].

Production by the end of April was 180 tons raised with 100 tons sold. The machinery on the dressing floors was working well but there was a scarcity of water as there had been no rain since Christmas with Retallick hoping for "some good genial spring showers".

A visit to the mines by Captain W. H. Williams of the Van Mines (Montgomeryshire) in April 1887, resulted in the following report. "The tips around the various shafts at Hurst would definately repay working and I saw more lead on the roads around Hurst than at some mines where thousands have been spent".

*Plate XIV. Brown's Engine shaft chimney. In the background lies the hamlet of Hurst with Shiney Row. To the left is the Home Farm with the gamekeeper's house at the end of the road.*

The two engines were working well at Cat Shaft but the foundations of the pumping engine needed strengthening and an additional boiler was required. The shaft itself was too small, and another shaft would be necessary as larger pumps would have to be installed as the workings went deeper. The dressing floors were well set out and capable of dressing 200 tons per month at present ore yeilds, depending on whether a sufficient supply of water could be found to allow day and night working. On the floors were two waterwheels, 31ft and 14ft diameter, two crushing mills, three self-acting jiggers, elevators and three round buddles.

Cat Shaft was now down to the 50 fms level and two 14" lifts had been added to the pumps in order to lift the water up to the Old Water Level.

Work was concentrated on the ground between the 40 fms and 50 fms levels, which was virtually untouched by the old man, and where the beds were very favourable, having chert on the sun side and limestone to the north. Golden, Shaft and Cleminson Veins were being worked by overhand stoping and rich ground had been found in the soles of Golden Vein which promised well for a future 60 fms level. Redshaft Vein had been found unproductive.

A total of 44 men were employed in stoping, 22 in driving with four men clearing the Water Level and four men clearing Hodgsons Sump from Queens Level down to Browns Rulleyway in order to ventilate the western part of the workings.

The present output was 120 tons per month which, after working expenses and royalty, left about £400 profit per month.

Future development depended on sinking Cat Shaft another 10 fms to give full command of the 12 fms lime at the western end of the mine and sinking another shaft 400 fms east of Cat Shaft. Captain Williams closed his report with a strong recommendation that Pryes Level be driven forward in order to unwater the whole field and lay open a vast area of unworked ground or consider driving a new level from Arkengarthdale.

In June, a Zennor buddle was in work on the dressing floors which greatly improved the output[52]. Working continued on the various veins but by August, the dryest season for 18 years, there was a lack of water on the floors, with a great accumulation of ore ready for dressing on the tips, and this, despite having raised the level of the dam by 5 ft. It was hoped that a portable engine could be purchased to get the floors working to avoid having to refill and retram the orestuff from the tips. The hot weather was also causing problems with ventilation. Not until September did the much-needed rain arrive to allow work to recommence on the floors.

Work had started meanwhile on the new shaft, called Brown's New Engine Shaft, which was seven fathoms down by September 1887[53]. The chimney was built and the engine house nearly ready. Transporting the boiler from Richmond to Hurst caused some problems and John Proctor of Hunton supplied the 18 horses to pull the boiler, with extra horses needed to get up the steep climb out of Marske[54].

By October, Brown's Shaft had holed through into Brown's Sump in Queens Level, the ground being in Main Chert and good for sinking, needing little timber. The water supply had been helped by raising the dam another four feet and more rain now meant that the backlog of ore could be processed.

The new shaft was down another 5½ fms by November, the engine house complete and the pumping and winding gear fixed. A semi-portable engine was in work on the floors with only 100 tons to clear. By December, a new drying house was completed which proved a great saving in coal.

In April 1888, the shaft had reached the Old Water Level at 33 fms and six men were cutting a platform ready to commence sinking into new ground. By June, the shaft was divided with the cage road, footway and spear rods in place.

John Retallick, the company's agent was convicted at Richmond County Police Court on June 16th 1888 and fined one pound for failing to send the ordinary returns in on time[55]. Whether this refers to Local or Income Taxes is not known but it was pointed out that he was liable to a £20 fine.

Work in the 50 fms level was held up by a large influx of water in December 1888, the men having to clear a piece of ground in order to run it off and the Cat Shaft pumps had to increase from 7 strokes to 14 strokes per minute to cope with the water. Brown's Engine Shaft was 7½ fms below the Water Level by January and this took some of the strain off the Cat Shaft pumps.

After the Arkengarthdale Mines the Hurst Mines were the only large producer left in Swaledale, all the other mines were either shut down or merely ticking over[55]. They were employing, for the first and only time in Swaledale, steam engines and all working faces producing good supplies of ore and promise of more unworked ground the deeper they went.

This rosy picture was painted at the expense of the Yorkshire Lead Mines Ltd and the cost of all this development work forced the company to declare an end to trading and a new company was set up called Hurst Lead Mines Ltd in January 1889. The reconstruction of this company was completed with an exchange of shares by February and the holders of £3,770 worth of debentures in Yorkshire Lead Mines accepting debentures with the new company. Most of the debts of the old company were cleared and £3,000 would be sufficient to complete development, three directors promising £1,600 and three shareholders a further £220. A total of 325 tons of ore had been raised since September last and all promised well for the new company.

Browns Engine Shaft was by March 11½ fms below the Old Water Level, leaving 5½ fms to reach the intended 16 fms level. Veins still producing were Golden, Red Shaft, Shaft, Cross Course, Cleminson and Akins Strings.

Work at Browns Shaft was delayed by snow at the end of March which prevented getting coal to the engine. An engine, air compressor and rock drill arrived in April 1889 to speed up the sinking in Browns Shaft, and by May, were in work and much needed, for they were sinking in the Underset Chert which was proving very difficult and must have caused a great deal of damage to the mens' lungs from the dust caused by the drill.

The sinking of the shaft was completed by July and two fms had been driven crosscutting south towards Cleminson Vein.

This work was then suspended along with all work east of Cat Shaft. All the men were put on sinking Cat Shaft to the same level as the Browns Shaft Sump. The direction now being taken by the directors seems to be going against all the practices set out by John Retallick. In September, he was ordered to stop the men getting ore by the fathom and set men to work in Hawkins String and Cross Course Vein stoping by the bing. Work at Cat Shaft was continuing where the Shaft Vein was starting to dip south. A Mr. Oxland took a sample of dressed ore which assayed at 76½% lead.

By October John Retallick had grown so dissilusioned at the way in which the directors were running the mines that he resigned and went to Marrick Park and took up farming. Work at Cat Shaft was 5 fms below the 50 fms level in the 12 fms Lime north of Shaft Vein and the ground, proving very unstable, needed large amounts of timber for support.

A fatal accident occurred in December when William Woodward, of Barf End at Hurst, was killed operating a crane[57]. The handle slipped and spinning round caught him on the forehead dashing out his brains and killing him instantly. He left a widow and four children and was much respected in the area being one of the Overseers for the Poor. He was a native of Gunnerside.

## Francis Morley's Law Suit Against Hurst Lead Mines Ltd.

Prior to the winding up of the Yorkshire Lead Mines Ltd., the company had asked Francis Morley for an extention of the lease for a further 31 years which, in view of the amount of capital the company had invested in the area, was not an unreasonable request. Morley had refused this lease but on what grounds is not known. This was one of the reasons for the winding up of the company. The Hurst Lead Mines Ltd, upon taking up the running of the mines, began to pay the royalty ore in undressed lead upon which Morley brought an action against the company in the Royal Court of Justice. Now resident at Stalybridge with his regiment, a firm of Manchester solicitors acted for Morley in the case.

In December 1889, an order for the winding up of the Hurst Lead Mining Company was passed by Mr. Justice Chitty in the Chancery Division of the High Court of Justice at the request of Mr. J. T. Kirkwood[58].

The hearing for Morley's case against the Hurst Lead Mining Co. took place on Thursday 13th February 1890[59]. Morley said that the company had begun to deliver his royalty ore in an undressed condition upon refusing them an extension of the lease. As he had no dressing machinery of his own and the smelt mill had never been worked by or for the present company it was impossible for him to make his ore marketable.

Council for the company alleged that by wording of the lease the ore was renderable in "smelting lead or undressed ore". When the lease was examined it was found that indeed the wording was as the company stated but a closer examination showed that the wording had been altered. Instead of the words "whether in smelted lead or in dressed ore" the sentence had the word smelted changed to smelting and the "in" had been scratched out and "un" inserted in its place.

In his defence, Morley stated that if he had agreed to take the ore in an undressed state he would never have leased the mills to the company. Also, the company had always paid the duty in marketable metal prior to the refusal of the extension. Up to 1885, the company had paid the dead rent of £100 as they had raised no ore, but after that time, the accounts showed the amounts of duty ore sold at Richmond and monies paid to him for this ore, but in 1888, for the half year ending June, the accounts showed a column headed "Proportion of lead ore set aside as Royalty" which was the first time the company tried to pay him in undressed ore.

The judge, Mr. Justice Kekwith, in his summing up, found that the rest of the lease did give the impression that the ore should be of marketable quality and that the mistake in the wording was not intentional. The judge found for Morley and that the 1/20th, 1/16th and 1/14th parts of ore be rendered marketable subject to the provision in the lease for substituting smelted lead at the option of the lessee. The judge did not award costs to Morley saying "I do not wish to lay blame on anyone, but with a little care this litigation could have been avoided. I do not wish to say who is responsible for that want of care and for that reason I do not think it is a case in which plaintiff ought to have any costs".

Morley's barrister accepted this but pointed out that the company had witheld the Colonel's ore for some time and they should have an account of ore due for Royalty; the company agreed there would be no problem with these accounts.

As directed by the court, this ore was set aside and dressed but found to be of insufficient quantity to make up the one sixteenth of the total yield of the mines for the past two years and the Receiver had to make up this deficiency from the companies stocks in order to avoid distraint.

Early in April 1890, the Official Receiver, Thomas Wilkins, reported on the mines which he was trying to keep going. The workings in the new 55 fms level had cut the vein below the area where rich workings had been found in the 50 fms level but no ore had been found. The ore in the various foreheads in the 50 fms level was not enough to pay the heavy costs of pumping in addition to the cost of raising and dressing the ore.

The present average expenditure of £240 per month; £100 was the cost of coal, cartage of coal, engine mens' wages and expense of the pumping machinery. £100 was spent on getting and dressing the ore and £40 in driving the new 55 fms level, other prospecting work and keeping the Old Water Level in repair. The ore being won was worth about £170 per month, so apart from the heavy costs of pumping, a fair profit could be returned. The workings at Cat Shaft were not extensive enough to employ a large number of men which might distribute the pumping costs over a large output of ore, and as labour in the area was scarce it commanded a fair price.

As the workings remained poor, Wilkins recommended that pumping cease at Cat Shaft and that Pryes Level be driven up under the field without delay at an approximate cost of £2,500 to £3,000 over two years. Also, to continue exploring for ore in those parts of the old workings accessible without steam pumping.

A meeting of the Debenture and Shareholders was called on the 29th of April 1890 but the development funds were not forthcoming and the company ceased trading. Some time later in 1890, another company, the Hurst Mine Syndicate was set up with a nominal capital of £4,000 in 400 £10 shares but this failed to get off the ground, thus bringing to an end the final glorious attempt to work the mines at Hurst.

At the Richmond County Police Court on April 3rd 1891, Mr. Francis Greathead, solicitor of Reeth, took out a summons against Hurst Lead Mines Ltd., for non payment of rates totalling £40 due to the Overseers of the Poor for the township of Marrick. He had previously applied for a warrant of distress to the bench but had been refused as the company was in liquidation. Although the Receiver, Thomas Wilkins, had written a note to him saying the company was in liquidation, this was, Mr. Greathead contended, insufficient proof of liquidation and the company had shown contempt by not sending an official to represent the company before the Bench[50].

Mr. Hodgson, one of the Overseers for Marrick, told the Bench that Wilkins had offered a horse and waggonette as part payment and the remainder would be paid after a final meeting of the creditors. It is not known whether this debt was ever cleared.

So the mines at Hurst never provided the relief from debt which had plagued the Morley family since 1816. Major-General Francis Morley was unable to clear his mortgage of £8,000 taken from Francis Riddell of Cheeseburn Grange, Newcastle and after his death in 1892, when he left the estate in trust to his son Henry Clervaux Chaytor Morley, who was only four at the time, the trustees decided to sell out to Francis Riddell in 1895.

The last attempt to restart mining at Hurst was in 1937 when a two year optional lease of the Pryes area was granted by Wilfred Jonathon Hird of Greenas Farm, Hurst, to the North Riding Lead Mining Company whose registered office was in Richmond[61].

Previously, this company had attempted to obtain a lease for the Old Gang Mines but were unable to agree terms with the lessors and so they turned their attention to the Hurst area.

The lease was granted on April the 6th 1937. The company was to pay an annual rental of £30, the first year's payments to be £10 on entry, £10 six months later and the final £10 after 12 months. The second yearly payments to be in two equal portions of £15 payable at six monthly intervals. They were to have an option of a twenty one year lease on six months notice.

The mine manager was Walter S. Rider of Beamish, Co. Durham, and he appointed as his foreman Archie Rule, a Cornishman who was working at the Fremington Chert Quarries but who had worked at mines in South America and Cornwall[62]. Archie brought with him from Fremington his son Howard, another Cornishman Benny Johns, Fremont Hutchinson and John William Longstaff. A local man Robert Hillary joined them in 1938.

After clearing and repairing the Pryes Level, a sump was started in the plate at the forehead of the main level in order to try the underlying limestone. Work was hard and slow as they had no machinery, all boring being done by hand with the deads being thrown down the old Engine Sump. Archie was paid £3-17s-6d per week and the men £2-10s. This trial had to be abandoned due to water seepage and the lack of a pump to drain it. They next tried rising into the upper beds but on breaking into the Old Man were again driven out by water.

All through this period they were hampered by lack of funds and no plans of the workings. A little chert was obtained and sent to Richmond Station in an old wagon, but in 1939, the venture was closed down, the men returning to Fremington Quarries.

## DOCUMENTARY SOURCES

| | |
|---|---|
| Hanby Holmes MSS. Ref. D/HH/6. Durham County Records Office. | DCRO. |
| Marrick Priory Papers, Brotherton Collection, University of Leeds. | MPPBL. |
| Marrick Priory Deeds, Archives Offices, University of Hull. | MPDUH. |
| Morley of Marrick and Draycott MSS, North Yorkshire County Record Office. | NYCRO. |

Reference to the *Craven Herald* which is a local newspaper, published in Skipton, Yorkshire, are drawn from research by Mike Gill.

## REFERENCES

1. NYCRO — ZHP. Map of the Manor of Marrick by Jackson, 1782.

2. Dunham, K.C. & Wilson, A. *Geology of the Northern Pennine Orefield,* Part 2. London, H.M.S.O., 1985, p.146.

   This is a misinterpretation of NYCRO Plan ZWX 17. The level ran towards Fremington Edge and not from it.

3. Gill, M.C. *Lead Mining in Yorkshire Before 1700.* British Mining No. 37, 1988, p.48.

4. Raistrick, A. Pers Comm Laurie, T. & Flemming, A. *Upland Settlement in Britain.* British Archaeological Reports, 142, 1985.

5. Speight, H. *Romantic Richmondshire,* London, 1897, p.207.

6. Smith, A.H. *Place Names of the North Riding of Yorkshire,* English Place Name Society, Cambridge University Press, Vol. 5, 1928.

7. MPPBL.

8. Bulmer, G. B. *Historical Notes on the Baronial House of Bulmer,* Published Privately. An undated copy may be found at Manchester City Library.

9. Borthwick Wills — January 2nd, 1531/32.

10. MPPBL — Inquisition.

11. MPPBL

12. Selden Society, Vol. 12, Select Cases in the Court of Requests, pp.201-205.

13. MPPBL — Correspondence relating to the ownership of Marrick Priory land.

14. Selden Society Vol. 12 and MPPBL

    Gill M.C. *The Yorkshire and Lancashire Lead Mines*. British Mining No. 33, 1987, p.54.

    These figures indicate a yield of 23 percent, which is very low. By 1630, smelters expected to get at least 50 percent. In consequence, the slags from boles were rich in lead and were reworked profitably by later smelters.

15. MPPBL — Depositions of evidence.

16. Raine's Marske.

17. Valor Ecclesiasticus, Record Commission Publication. A national survey of monastic lands at the time of Henry VIII.

18. Hartley/Ingleby Collection, since deposited at the NYCRO.

19. This shows that lead smelters were aware of the value of cinders (coke) for smelting slags before they were used for iron smelting by Abraham Derby.

20. NYCRO — Morley of Marrick MSS.

21. NYCRO — ZAZ Mining.

22. MPPBL — Letters from Reuben Orton to John Blackburne.

23. Bevan-Evans, M. *Gladlys and Flintshire Lead Mining in the Eighteenth Century*, Studies in Flintshire Records No. 1, Hawarden, 1963, p.12.

    Some of the earliest cupola (reverberatory) furnaces were in Flintshire. Daniel Peck built some near Mold, during the 1760s, and they were later used by the London Lead Company at its Gadlys works. They were introduced into Derbyshire (at Olda) and the North Pennines in the mid 1730s. The Marrick Cupola was, therefore, a very early example.

24. MPPBL — (6/12/1703) Letter from John Copperthwaite to John Blackburne.

25. MPPBL — Ingleton Lease, 21/9/1703. Tyson, L.O. *Lead Mining at Ingleton*, Dalesman, July 1986, Vol. 48, No. 4, p.289.

26. MPPBL — Gyles Blackburne's notebook.

27. NYCRO Draycott MSS. Further background to the sale of the Cupola and Marrick Priory may be found in the MPPBL.

28. NYCRO — ZAZ 6. Raine's — Marske, p.285.

29. NYCRO — ZFY 40.

30. Raistrick, A. *The London (Quaker) Lead Company Mines in Yorkshire*, N.C.M.R.S. Memoirs, Vol. 2 No. 3, September 1973, pp.127-131.

    Raistrick, A. *The Lead Industry of Wensleydale & Swaledale*, Vol. 2: The Smelt Mills, Moorland, Hartington, 1975, p.38.

31. NYCRO — ZHP. Map of the Manor of Marrick by Jackson, 1782.

32. Facts and Figures Against Groundless Assertions. Harland v Morley. Submission by John Harland, dated 1854. Photocopy in author's possession.

33. Coates MSS. Hurst Candle, Powder and Day Book: 1827-53.

34. DCRO — D/HH/6/4/100.

35. The term draught refers to a number of kibbles or waggons but its value is unclear.

36. Harland — Facts and Figures.

37. NYCRO — Morley of Marrick Papers.

38. DCRO — D/HH/6/4/7 and original sale bill, in author's possession.

39. British Parliamentary Papers — *Mining Accidents,* Session 1864. Epitome of Evidence, Vol. 7, p.407-409 and Vol. 8, p.346.

40. NYCRO — Morley of Marrick Papers, Microfilm No. 1332.

41. NYCRO — Morley of Marrick Papers, Microfilm No. 1316.

42. NYCRO — Morley of Marrick Papers, Microfilm No. 1316.

43. Craven Herald, July 22nd, 1882, p.5, Col.2.

44. Mining Journal, October 21st, 1882, p.1273. Report by John Retallick.

45. Mining Journal, July 5th, 1884, p.779.

46. Mining Journal, January 24th, 1885, p.93.

47. Mining Journal, June 27th, 1885, p.734.

48. Mining Journal, August 27th, 1887, p.1057.

49. Mining Journal, December 18th, 1886, p.1470.

50. Northern Echo, February 12th, 1887, p.1.

51. Mining Journal, April 9th, 1887, p.438.

52. Mining Journal, June 4th, 1887, p.691.

53. Mining Journal, August 27th, 1887, p.1057.

54. Craven Herald, September 3rd, 1887, p.6, col.4 and L. Barker pers. comm.

55. Craven Herald, June 16th, 1888, p.5, col.3.

56. Burt, R. Atkinson, M. Waite, P. Burnley, R. *The Yorkshire Mineral Statistics 1845-1913.* Exeter, University of Exeter, 1982.

57. Craven Herald, December 6th, 1889, p.3, col.5.

58. Craven Herald, December 13th, 1889, p.6, col.2.

59. NYCRO — Morley of Marrick Papers.

60. Craven Herald, April 3rd, 1891, p.6, col.3.

61. DCRO — D/H/6/4/121 and Mr H. Rule pers. com.

62. H. Rule and C. Bray pers. com.

# GENERAL READING

Aveling, H. *Northern Catholics,* London, Chapman, 1966.

Burke, J.B. *Dictionary of Landed Gentry,* London, Harrison, 1838.

Burke, J. *A Geneological and Heraldic History of the Commons of Great Britain and Ireland.* London, Bentley, 1833.

Burton, J. *Monasticon Eboracanse* York, 1758, pp.269–271.

Clarkson, C. *The History of Richmond,* 1821, the author, pp.316–321.

Clough, R.T. *Lead Smelting Mills of the Yorkshire Dales.* Keighley, the author, 1962.

Dictionary of National Biography. Oxford University Press, 1917.

Dugdale, W. *Monasticon Anglicanum,* London, 1846, pp.244–247.

Dunham, K.C. & Wilson, A.A. *Geology of the Northern Pennine Orefield,* Volume 2, London, H.M.S.O., 1985.

Fieldhouse, R. & Jennings, B. *A History of Richmond and Swaledale,* Phillimore, London, 1978.

Gale, R. Registrum Honoris de Richmond, 1722.

Harrison, P. History of the Wapentake of Gilling West, pp.244–247.

Hartley, M. *Yorkshire Heritage,* Dent, London, 1950.

Hartley, M. & Ingilby, J. *A Dales Heritage,* 1982.

Raine, J. *Marske,* Yorkshire Archaeological and Topographical Journal, Volume 6, 1881, pp.227f.

Raistrick, A. *The Wharton Mines in Swaledale,* North Yorkshire Record Office Publication, Northallerton, Volume 32, 1982.

Raistrick, A. & Jennings, B. *A History of Lead Mining in the Pennines,* London, Longmans, 1965.

Stapleton, T. *Charters and History of Marrick Priory,* Collectanea, Topographica et Genealogica, Volume 5, 1838.

Tyson, L.O. *The Hurst Lead Mining Field, Swaledale.* British Mining No. 23, N.M.R.S., pp.61–74.

Victoria County History of the North Riding of Yorkshire. Gilling West Wapontake, Volume 1. London, Constable, 1914, pp.97–104.

Victoria County History Yorkshire. Marrick Priory, Volume 1. University of London, Institute of Historical Studies, 1974, pp.117f.

**IN CHANCERY.**

Between {
JOHN BAILEY LANGHORNE & OTHERS, Plaintiffs.
JOHN HARLAND & OTHERS, Defendants.

---

# TO BE SOLD BY AUCTION,

## Pursuant to a Decree of the High Court of Chancery

MADE IN THE ABOVE CAUSE, WITH THE APPROBATION OF THE JUDGE TO WHOSE COURT THE SAME IS ATTACHED,

# AT THE BUCK INN, IN REETH,

### IN THE NORTH RIDING OF THE COUNTY OF YORK,

## ON FRIDAY, THE 6th DAY OF FEBRUARY, 1857,

### AT TWO O'CLOCK IN THE AFTERNOON,

### EITHER TOGETHER OR IN THREE LOTS,

---

BY

# MESSRS THOMAS & JOHN WETHERELL,

## AUCTIONEERS,

---

ALL THE

# SHARES & INTEREST OF FRAS. MORLEY,

### LATE OF MARRICK PARK, ESQ., DECEASED,

OF AND IN THOSE VALUABLE

# LEASEHOLD LEAD MINES

IN THE

### MANOR OF GRINTON, IN THE NORTH RIDING OF YORKSHIRE,

KNOWN BY THE RESPECTIVE NAMES OF

### "THE GRINTON MOOR MINE," "THE WHITASIDE MINE," AND "THE SUMMER LODGE MINE."

---

The Mining Fields may be inspected on application to the Agents on the spot, and Particulars and Conditions of Sale may be had in London of Messrs SHUM, WILSON, & CROSSMAN, 3, King's Road, Bedford Row ; of Messrs WESTMACOTT & F. W. BLAKE, 28, John Street, Bedford Row ; and of Messrs NORRIS & ALLEN, 20, Bedford Row ; and in the Country, of Messrs LANGHORNE & TOMLIN, Mr. G. S. HARRISON, and Mr. THOMAS BRADLEY, Junior, Solicitors, Richmond, Yorkshire, and of the AUCTIONEERS.